The Institution of Civil Engineers

The Engineering and Construction Contract

An NEC document

Guidance notes

Thomas Telford, London

Published for the Institution of Civil Engineers by Thomas Telford Services Ltd, Thomas Telford House, 1 Heron Quay, London E14 4JD.

The NEC System is published as a series of documents of which this is one.

The Engineering and Construction Contract is part of the New Engineering Contract (NEC) family of contracts. The NEC contracts were originally designed and drafted by Dr Martin Barnes of Coopers & Lybrand with the assistance of:

Professor J G Perry
P A Baird
T H Nicholson
A Norman
T W Weddell

The Engineering and Construction Contract has been derived from the New Engineering Contract by the NEC Panel. The membership of the Panel was:

Dr Martin Barnes
Andrew Baird
Les Eames
Tom Nicholson
Michael Noakes
Professor John Perry
Nigel Shaw
Bill Weddell

ISBN (series) 0 7277 2081 3

ISBN (this document) 0 7277 2079 1

Consultative edition 1991
First edition 1993
Second edition November 1995
Reprinted 1996

British Library Cataloguing in Publication Data for this publication is available from the British Library.

Printed and bound in Great Britain by MPG Information Division, Unwin Brothers Limited, The Gresham Press, Old Woking, Surrey.

FOREWORD

'A Fundamental Review'

In September 1985 the Council of the Institution of Civil Engineers approved a recommendation from its Legal Affairs Committee 'to lead a fundamental review of alternative contract strategies for civil engineering design and construction with the objective of identifying the needs for good practice'. Preparation of a specification of a new style contract was commissioned in July 1986. The work was carried out by Dr Martin Barnes, then of Martin Barnes Project Management, now a partner of Coopers & Lybrand, with the assistance of Dr John Perry, then of the Project Management Group at the University of Manchester Institute of Science and Technology, and now Beale Professor and Head of the School of Civil Engineering at the University of Birmingham.

The specification was submitted to the Legal Affairs Committee in December 1986 and, after modification, presented to a limited audience in September 1987. In June 1988 the Council decided to develop a draft of the new style contract through a working group of members of the Institution, representatives of contractors, consulting engineers and employers. The drafting team was led by Dr Martin Barnes.

Consultation

A consultative version of the New Engineering Contract was published in January 1991. Comments were received from a large number of organisations and individuals including employers, contractors, consulting engineers, surveyors and lawyers. Discussion also took place at seminars and conferences and with various organisations.

The consultative version of the New Engineering Contract was used in a number of different types of contract in various countries including the United Kingdom, South Africa, Hong Kong and Belize. Valuable feedback was received. A first edition of the New Engineering Contract was published in March 1993.

Latham — 'Constructing the Team'

In July 1994, Sir Michael Latham produced his report 'Constructing The Team'. This report was commissioned by the UK Government in collaboration with the construction industry and its professions. It recommended that the New Engineering Contract should be adopted by clients in both the private and public sectors and suggested that it should become a national standard contract across the whole of engineering and construction work generally.

Following the publication of the Latham report, the Institution of Civil Engineers decided to bring forward the publication of a second edition of the New Engineering Contract. This second edition includes a large number of small refinements to the first edition prompted by further comment on the first edition and by feedback from projects on which the first edition has been used. Extensive changes have been made to the insurance and adjudication provisions. It also includes the changes recommended in the Latham report in order that the New Engineering Contract should comply with the principles for a modern contract set out in the report and that it should be entirely appropriate for wide use.

One of the recommendations in the Latham report was that the name of the document should be changed. This is why, in the second edition, the name of the main contract has been changed to Engineering and Construction Contract. This now forms part of the NEC family of contracts which includes the Professional Services Contract, the Engineering and Construction Subcontract and the Adjudicator's Contract.

CONTENTS

INTRODUCTION

Background

The NEC Engineering and Construction Contract (ECC) (previously the New Engineering Contract) has been developed to meet the current and future needs for a form of contract to be used in engineering and construction generally, which is an improvement on existing standard contracts in a number of ways.

Purpose of guidance notes

The purpose of these guidance notes is to explain the background to the ECC, the reasons for some of its provisions and to provide guidance on how to use it.

Neither the flow charts nor the guidance notes are contract documents, nor are they part of the ECC. They should not be used for legal interpretation of the meaning of the ECC or the ECS.

Objectives

The objectives for the design of the NEC contracts were to make improvements under three main headings.

Flexibility

The ECC is intended

- to be used for engineering and construction work containing any or all of the traditional disciplines such as civil, electrical, mechanical and building work.
- to be used whether the Contractor has some design responsibility, full design responsibility or no design responsibility.
- to provide all the normal current options for types of contract such as competitive tender (where the Contractor is committed to his offered prices), target contracts, cost reimbursable contracts and management contracts.
- to be used in the United Kingdom and in other countries.

All the commonly used standard conditions of contract from the various sectors of engineering and construction have been reviewed in the course of designing the ECC. Some of their provisions which were peculiar to particular sectors have been omitted where they are better included in the Works Information. Where they are essential, they have been included in the ECC itself. For example, the need to make full provision for off-site manufacture and testing of work which is characteristic of mechanical and electrical contracts has been included in the ECC.

In order to achieve uniformity across these sectors, some changes of terminology have been necessary. One example is that the word 'Equipment' is used for what, in the building and civil engineering sectors, has in the past been called 'Constructional Plant'. The word 'Plant' is used in the ECC as it is customarily used in all the other engineering sectors. The traditional civil engineering and building term 'temporary works' is covered by 'Equipment' as defined in ECC Clause 11.2(11) and therefore is not used.

Clarity and simplicity

Although a legal document, the ECC is written in ordinary language. As far as possible, it uses only words which are in common use so that it is easily understood by people whose first language is not English and that it can easily be translated into other languages. It has few sentences which contain more than 40 words. Generally, longer sentences have been subdivided using bullet points to permit easier understanding. In the areas of insurance, disputes and termination, some phrases or terms which have a specific legal meaning have been retained.

It is arranged and organised in a structure which helps the user to gain familiarity with its contents. More importantly, the actions by the parties which follow from use of the ECC are defined precisely so that there should be few disputes about who is to do what and how.

The design of the ECC is based upon flow charts of the procedures to be followed by the parties named in the contract. One of the benefits of this approach to drafting has been that opportunities could be taken for simplifying the structure of the contract as well as ensuring that the procedures were not open-ended or conflicting. For example, almost all circumstances which may give rise to additional payment to the Contractor are identified as compensation events. The procedure for dealing with these events is mainly set out in the core clauses and includes review of both the cost and time implications. This contrasts with traditional forms of contract in which the procedure for compensation is different depending upon the nature of each event.

The initial impact of reading the ECC may not convey its full simplicity, in part because a number of newly defined expressions are used. The quantity of text used is much less than existing standard forms and the amount of text needed to give effect to the options is small.

The number of clauses used and the amount of text are less than in many standard forms. The ECC neither requires nor contains cross-references between clauses.

A fundamental objective of the ECC is that its use should minimise the incidence of disputes. Thus words like 'fair', 'reasonable' and 'opinion' have been used as little as possible. This does not mean that the flexibility of administering the contract has been reduced. For example, in most instances where the Project Manager is required to make a decision, the basis of his decision is stated in the contract. This will significantly reduce uncertainty about the outcome of the contract. This benefits the Contractor without constraining the freedom of action of the Project Manager acting on behalf of the Employer.

Stimulus to good management

This is perhaps the most important characteristic of the ECC. Every procedure has been designed so that its implementation should contribute to rather than detract from the effectiveness of management of the work. This aspect of ECC is founded upon the proposition that foresighted, co-operative management of the interactions between the parties can shrink the risks inherent in construction work. Developments in project management techniques and their implementation over the past 20 years have moved faster than the evolution of forms of contract. With the ECC, it is now possible to build arrangements for the different parties to contribute to the management of a project upon improved practices and to motivate all parties, by means of the contract, to apply such practices to their work.

In total, the ECC is intended to provide a modern method for employers, designers, contractors and project managers to work collaboratively. It also enables them to achieve their own objectives more consistently than has been possible using older forms of contract. Use of the ECC is intended to lead to a much reduced risk to the Employer of cost and time overruns and of poor performance of the completed projects. It should also lead to a much increased likelihood of achieving a profit for the Contractor, subcontractors and suppliers.

The two principles on which the ECC is based and which impact upon the objective of stimulating good management are:

- foresight applied collaboratively mitigates problems and shrinks risk, and
- clear division of function and responsibility helps accountability and motivates people to play their part.

A secondary but important theme is that people will be motivated to play their part in collaborative management if it is in their commercial and professional interest to do so. Reliance need not be placed upon exhortation either within the contract or outside it.

Uncertainty about what is to be done and about how the unexpected arising in the course of construction will affect what has to be done are inevitable in construction projects. The ECC allocates clearly the risks arising in these ways between the parties. However, its main task is to reduce the incidence of those risks by application of collaborative foresight. In this way, it aims to improve the outcome of projects generally for parties whose interests might seem to be opposed.

The procedures in the ECC are designed to stimulate good management. Prominent examples of these are the early warning procedure and the way in which compensation events are dealt with. Compensation events are events which may lead to the payment to the *Contractor* being changed or the Completion Date being delayed.

A principle of the ECC is that the *Project Manager*, acting on behalf of the *Employer* and in communication with him, should be presented with options for dealing with the problem from which he can choose, directed by the interests of the *Employer*. The *Contractor* should be unaffected by the choice made. To achieve this, the valuation of compensation events is based upon a forecast of the impact which the change or problem will have upon the cost to the *Contractor* of carrying out the work – as forecast by him at the time the event is assessed. Where, as is often the case, alternative ways of dealing with the problem are possible, the *Contractor* prepares quotations for different ways of tackling the problem. The *Project Manager* selects one on the basis of which will best serve the interests of the *Employer*. In some cases this will be the lowest cost solution, in others it might be the least delay solution.

The change to the Prices for the work is based upon the quotation. The *Contractor* carries the risk if his forecast of cost impact turns out to be wrong, but the *Employer* has a firm commitment. The risk to the *Contractor* of this method of pricing is conceptually similar to the risk he takes when pricing work at tender. It is a lesser risk because he is able to forecast costs much more accurately at the time that the problem is identified than he would have been able to do at the tender stage.

This arrangement is intended to stimulate foresight, to enable the *Employer* to make rational decisions about changes to the work with reasonable certainty of their cost and time implications, and to put a risk on the *Contractor* which is tolerable and which motivates him to manage the new situation efficiently. An important by-product is that few issues relating to valuation of the work or extensions of time are left to be settled after the event.

This approach has pervaded the drafting of the ECC and is the basis for most of the procedures which it contains. In designing the ECC, the motivation of each party in each action he is to take has been considered against good management criteria. Because this is motivation-driven, it does not appear in the words of the ECC itself but it is intended to result directly from the way in which the procedures are operated.

A typical aspect of this characteristic is the way in which the ECC makes use of the programme for design, construction and installation. Many of the detailed procedures rely upon the fact that an up-to-date and realistic programme maintained by the *Contractor* is used in joint decision-making between him and the *Project Manager*. The use of the programme (which includes method and resource statements) is defined in some detail and in such a way that, again, the *Contractor* is motivated to keep it up-to-date and realistic. He is not simply exhorted to do so.

Subcontracts

The ECC has been designed on the assumption that work may be subcontracted. A standard form of subcontract called the NEC Engineering and Construction Subcontract (ECS) has been published. This is very similar to the ECC but uses appropriate names for the parties and has a small number of additional provisions appropriate to a subcontract.

Use of the same text in the main contract and the subcontract provides certain back-to-back protection for main contractors using the ECS. It also has the convenience that *Contractors*' and *Subcontractors*' staff do not have to become familiar with two different sets of text and procedure. There is nothing to prevent a subcontract using a different option from that used in the main contract. An obvious example of this is where the main contract uses the management contract option but the subcontract uses one of the more conventional options. Option F (Management contract) has not been included in the ECS.

Some other changes

Two specific changes from conventional construction practice deserve mention. Firstly, subcontractors cannot be nominated. This change is made in order to simplify contract arrangements and to eliminate the clouding of responsibilities which nomination causes. Elimination of this clouding should not only reduce disputes but strengthen the motivation of the parties to manage their activities. An *Employer* who has reasons for using a particular contractor for part of the works can use the ECC for a direct contract alongside other contractors.

Secondly, the financial control document in the ECC can be either a traditional bill of quantities or an activity schedule. The *activity schedule* is a list of items with lump sum prices. The total price for the work to be done is divided between each of the items. This is a simpler document to prepare and use than the traditional bill. Neither document is used in the ECC for any purpose other than assessing payments due to the Contractor.

Application of the ECC

Although, at first reading, the ECC may appear to be similar to existing standard forms, to rely upon such an impression would be wrong. As the flow charts show, most procedures are based on good management practice and often differ from current practice in some engineering and building disciplines. This is not change for the sake of change, as the application of the principles of the ECC in pursuit of its objectives has left very little of conventional practice to be incorporated unchanged.

The user of the ECC must, therefore, study it carefully, as the words are not simply different expressions of familiar practice.

The ECC is drafted in a simple and clear style, but its differences from current practice mean that some explanation and consideration of how it will work is necessary when it is first used. These guidance notes are essential reading for people using the ECC for the first time. They will continue to be useful in training people coming into the management of projects in how to make best use of the Engineering and Construction Contract as part of the NEC System. The published flow charts should also be referred to as illustrations of the procedures on which the ECC is based.

The published documents

The convention of using italics for terms which are identified in the Contract Data of the ECC and capital initials for terms defined in the ECC has been used in these guidance notes.

Arrangement of the ECC

The ECC includes the following sections of text:

- the core clauses,
- the main option clauses,
- the secondary option clauses,
- the Schedules of Cost Components and
- the Contract Data formats.

Other documents when using the ECC will include:

- the Works Information
- the Site Information
- the Accepted Programme
- documents resulting from choosing secondary options such as Performance Bond (if submitted before Contract Date)

Depending on the choice of main option, the documents may also include:

- an activity schedule or
- a bill of quantities.

The Schedule of Cost Components is a complete identification of components of cost which is not varied from one contract to another. It is used to avoid uncertainty where Actual Cost has to be assessed in connection with any of the procedures of the contract. It is not priced.

The Contract Data are selected and completed for each contract. These data identify such things as the completion dates, the contract-specific documents (e.g. specifications and drawings), interest rates and price adjustment indices to be used.

The following volumes are published with the second edition (1995) of the ECC:

- the complete Engineering and Construction Contract (ECC),
- the NEC Engineering and Construction Subcontract (ECS),
- the flow charts,
- these guidance notes and
- six merged versions of the ECC, one for each main option.

The complete ECC

This volume contains all the clauses and schedules comprising the ECC including

- core clauses — common to all contracts,
- clauses for each of the main options A to F — one of which should be chosen for a particular contract,
- clauses for each of the secondary options G to Z — each available, if required, for a particular contract,
- Schedule of Cost Components, applicable to main options A to E,
- Shorter Schedule of Cost Components, applicable to main options A to E, and
- Contract Data formats parts one and two.

The EC Subcontract

This volume contains all the clauses (core and options), and schedules constituting the EC Subcontract, i.e. the form of subcontract which is the equivalent of the complete ECC and which is compatible with it. It is intended to be used for subcontracts which are let where the main contract is the ECC.

Flow charts

The flow charts show the procedural logic on which the ECC is based. They are available for reference in conjunction with these guidance notes.

Merged versions

Each merged version includes the clauses for the relevant main option located in their appropriate places amongst the core clauses. Thus, the conditions for each main option can be read together. The main option clauses are in bold print for easy identification.

The merged versions also include

- those secondary option clauses which can be used with each main option,
- the Contract Data, adapted for each main option,
- the two Schedules of Cost Components (except for Option F where they are not required). For Options A to E, these schedules differ only in the introductory paragraph.

Clause numbering

The ECC is arranged in nine sections:

1 General
2 The *Contractor*'s main responsibilities
3 Time
4 Testing and Defects
5 Payment
6 Compensation events
7 Title
8 Risks and insurance
9 Disputes and termination

The first digit of a clause number, whether for a core clause or a main option clause, is the number of the section to which the clause belongs.

The paragraphs within each clause are numbered by the digits after the decimal point. For convenience, a paragraph is frequently referred to in these guidance notes as a clause, e.g. Clause 61.3 means paragraph 3 of Clause 61.

Where a clause or paragraph is used in more than one main option, the same number is used. The number of a paragraph, whether core or optional, is unique to the text of the paragraph.

The secondary option clauses are numbered separately and are prefixed by the option letter.

The tables in Appendix 1 of these guidance notes illustrate the integration of the main option clauses and paragraphs within the core clauses and list the secondary option clauses.

Project organisation

The project organisation assumed in the ECC involves the participants shown in Figure 1.

The ECC is used for the contract between the *Employer* and the *Contractor*. The ECS may be used for the *Contractor*'s subcontracts. The NEC Professional Services Contract may be used for contracts with the *Project Manager*, the designers or the *Supervisor*. The NEC Adjudicator's Contract is used for the contract between the *Employer* and *Contractor* (jointly) and the *Adjudicator*. It may also be used in subcontracts using the ECS and in NEC Professional Services Contracts.

The roles of the *Project Manager*, designers and *Supervisor* may be combined where the objectives of the *Employer* are served by so doing. Similarly, any or all of these three roles may be taken by employees of the *Employer*. The role of the *Adjudicator* should neither be combined with another role nor taken by an employee of the *Employer*.

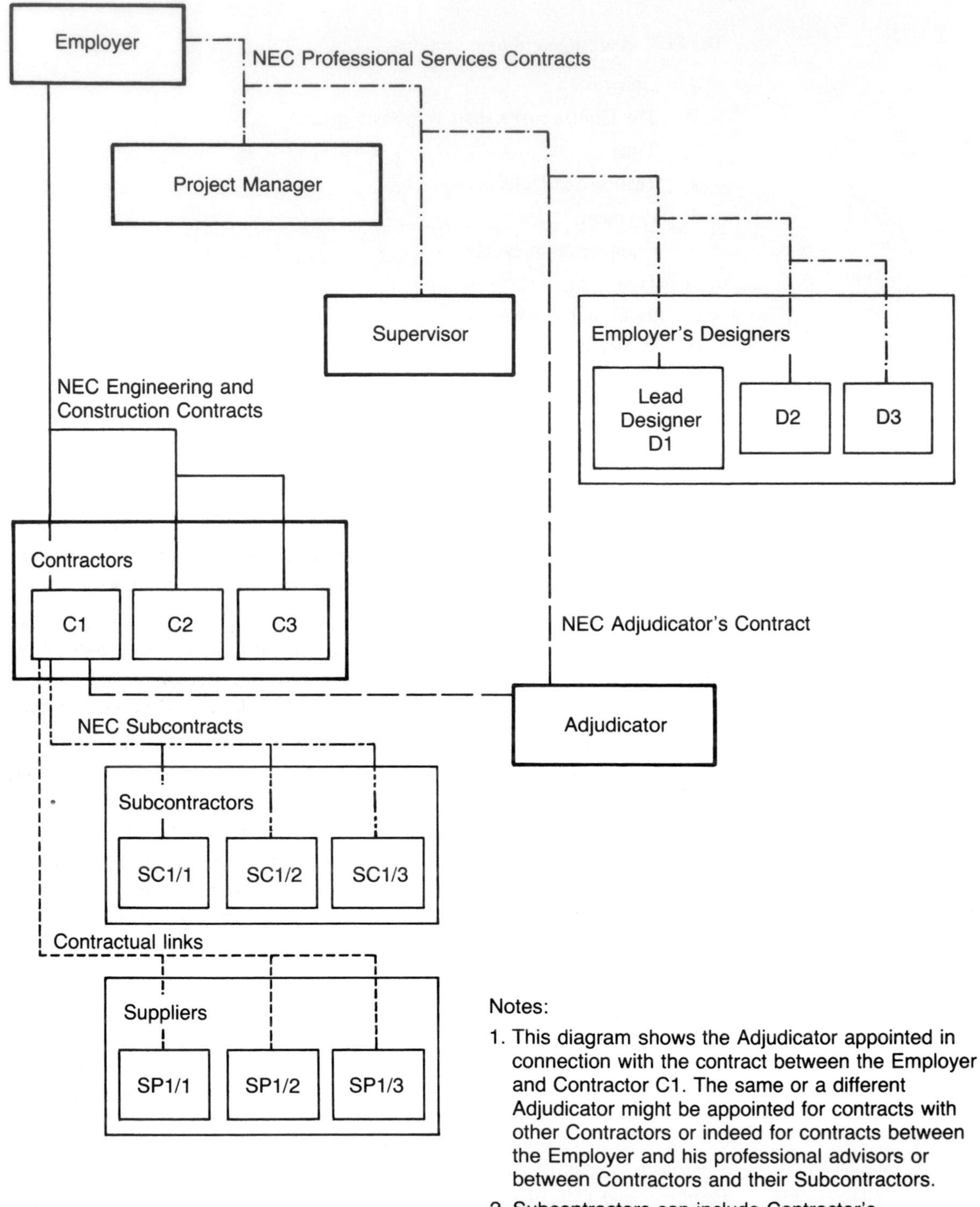

Notes:

1. This diagram shows the Adjudicator appointed in connection with the contract between the Employer and Contractor C1. The same or a different Adjudicator might be appointed for contracts with other Contractors or indeed for contracts between the Employer and his professional advisors or between Contractors and their Subcontractors.
2. Subcontractors can include Contractor's Designers who might be appointed under an NEC Professional Services Contract between the Contractor and the Designer rather than the NEC Subcontract shown in this diagram.

Figure 1. The NEC System — key players and contractual links

Roles and duties

The ECC sets out the responsibilities and roles of the following parties:

- the *Employer*,
- the *Project Manager*,
- the *Supervisor*,
- the *Contractor*,
- the Subcontractor and
- the *Adjudicator*

Separate functions of *Employer*'s designer and *Contractor*'s designer are assumed but not mentioned in the contract.

The role played by the Engineer, Architect or Supervising Officer in other standard forms is divided between the *Project Manager*, the *Supervisor*, the *Employer*'s designer and the *Adjudicator*.

The *Project Manager*

The *Project Manager* is appointed by the *Employer*, either from his own staff or from outside. His role within the ECC is to manage the contract for the *Employer* with the intention of achieving the *Employer*'s objectives for the completed project.

The *Employer* will normally appoint a project manager in the feasibility study stages of a project. His duties may then also include acting on behalf of the *Employer* and advising him on the procurement of design, on estimates of costs and time, on the merits of alternative schemes and on choosing the most appropriate contract strategy.

As contracts are placed for construction work, it is preferable to appoint the person or organisation already appointed for the whole project to act as the *Project Manager* on a particular contract. However, it is essential that the *Project Manager* for a particular contract is sufficiently close to the work and has the time and authority to carry out his duties effectively. On very large projects, especially those including several contracts, it may be necessary to appoint a different *Project Manager* for each contract or for the *Project Manager* to delegate his responsibilities for some of the contracts.

The ECC places considerable authority in the hands of the *Project Manager*. It assumes that he has the *Employer*'s authority to carry out the actions and make the decisions which are required of him. If his contract with the *Employer* constrains him in any way, as for example in the case of a limit on the amount which the *Project Manager* may authorise as a compensation event assessment, it is the responsibility of the *Project Manager* to ensure that all the approvals are given in time to enable him to comply with the time periods set out in the ECC. If such approvals by the *Employer* are not given, the *Contractor* has the right to raise the matter with the *Adjudicator*. It is not advisable to state limits on the *Project Manager*'s authority in the additional conditions of contract as this will make settlement of disputes difficult.

The *Project Manager* is free to seek the *Employer*'s views as much or as little as his relationship and contract with the *Employer* requires. He will normally maintain close contact with the *Employer* so that his decisions reflect the *Employer*'s business objectives. He has authority to change the work, to instruct the *Contractor*, and generally to apply his managerial and engineering judgement. Positive management from both sides is encouraged.

The contractual role of the *Project Manager* is defined in terms of the actions and decisions he is to take. He is constrained from acting unreasonably in this role by statements of the basis on which he is to make each type of decision but not what decisions he is to make. If the *Contractor* believes that any of the *Project Manager*'s actions or decisions is not in accordance with the contract, he may refer it to the *Adjudicator* (Clause 90.1).

Perhaps the strongest feature of the ECC which stimulates co-operation rather than adversarial activity is the fact that the *Contractor* is little concerned with the way the *Project Manager* decides to deal with problems which are the *Employer*'s responsibility. If the *Contractor*'s eventual payment is largely secure, he is not encouraged to make the worst of any problems which arise, either as regards their effect upon cost or upon the timing of the work. This feature is strengthened by the flexibility available to the *Employer* and the *Project Manager* in their pre-contract choice of main option for a particular contract ranging from price commitment to cost reimbursable. The ECC permits this choice of contract strategy without the need to resort to different standard forms.

Designers

Designers for the *Employer*'s design are appointed by the *Employer*. If several designers are appointed, possibly covering different disciplines, a lead designer should be appointed.

If the design of the *works* depends on a process technology, for which the *Employer* has a licence, he will need to provide appropriate access to it as part of his contract with the designer (and also for management purposes in the *Project Manager*'s contract).

The designer's role is to develop the design to meet the *Employer*'s objectives to the point where tenders for construction are to be invited. If a 'design and construct' contract is envisaged, the *Employer*'s designer's role is restricted largely to providing a performance specification together with standards for design and materials which he may wish to specify for inclusion in the Works Information.

Under the ECC the *Employer*'s designer is not referred to in the contract between the *Employer* and the *Contractor*. However, the *Employer* should ensure that the *Project Manager*'s brief includes management of the designer's activities. The *Project Manager* should have ready access to the designer for advice.

The *Supervisor*

The *Supervisor* is appointed by the *Employer* for a particular contract. He can be an in-house person or someone from outside. His role is defined in the ECC in terms of the actions and decisions he is to take. Essentially, his role is to check that the *works* are constructed in accordance with the contract. It is similar to that of a resident engineer or architect who may be assisted by an inspector or clerk of works. In some circumstances it would be appropriate for the clerk of works to carry out this role.

Like those of the *Project Manager*, a disputed action by the *Supervisor* can be referred by the *Contractor* to the *Adjudicator* (Clause 90.1).

The *Adjudicator*

The *Adjudicator* is appointed jointly by the *Employer* and the *Contractor* for the contract. The *Employer* should insert his choice of *Adjudicator* in part one of the Contract Data. If the *Contractor* does not agree with the choice, a suitable person will be the subject of discussion and agreement before the Contract Date. Alternatively, the *Employer* may propose a list of acceptable names, and the successful tenderer may be asked to select one of them to be *Adjudicator*. Some *Employer*s may prefer the tenderers to propose suitable names.

The *Adjudicator* becomes involved, only when a dispute is referred to him. As a person independent of both *Employer* and *Contractor*, he is required to give a decision on the dispute, within stated time limits. If either Party does not accept his decision, they may proceed to the *tribunal* (either arbitration or the courts). Under the Adjudicator's Contract, payment of the *Adjudicator*'s fee is shared equally by the Parties.

CONTRACT STRATEGY

Choosing the strategy

The *Employer* (usually advised by the *Project Manager*) chooses the contract strategy for the project. He should review his choice later, when he starts preparing the tender documents for each contract. Factors taken into account in deciding what type of contract to use from within the NEC family include the following:

- who has the necessary design expertise,
- whether there is particular pressure to complete quickly,
- how important is performance of the complete *works*,
- whether certainty of final cost is more important than lowest final cost,
- where can a risk be best managed,
- what total risk is tolerable for contractors,
- how important is cross contract co-ordination to achievement of project objectives, and
- whether the *Employer* has good reasons for himself selecting specialist contractors or suppliers for parts of the work.

The result of these considerations should be a statement of the chosen contract strategy comprising the following:

- a schedule of the parts of the project which will be let as separate contracts,
- for each contract – a statement of the stages of work which it will include covering management, design, manufacture, erection, construction, installation, testing and commissioning as appropriate, and
- a statement of the ECC main option which will be used for each contract.

The ECC main options offer different basic allocations of risk between the *Employer* and the *Contractor*.

- Options A and B are priced contracts in which the risks of being able to carry out the work at the agreed prices are largely borne by the *Contractor*.
- Options C and D are target contracts in which the financial risks are shared by the *Employer* and the *Contractor* in an agreed proportion.
- Options E and F are two types of cost reimbursable contract in which the financial risk is largely borne by the *Employer*.

All the main options can be used with the boundary between design by the *Employer* and design by the *Contractor* set to suit the chosen strategy. If the Works Information set down by the *Employer* is only a performance specification, most of the design will be done by the *Contractor* (effectively a 'design and construct' contract). If the Works Information includes detailed drawings and specifications, little design remains for the *Contractor* to complete.

An advantage of using the ECC is that, whatever variations in strategy are adopted, most of the procedures, based upon the core clauses of the ECC, will be common to all contracts.

The main options

There are six types of payment mechanism available in the main options:

Option A	Priced contract with activity schedule
Option B	Priced contract with bill of quantities
Option C	Target contract with activity schedule
Option D	Target contract with bill of quantities
Option E	Cost reimbursable contract
Option F	Management contract

Each option uses different arrangements for payment to the *Contractor* as each option allocates risk differently between the *Employer* and the *Contractor*.

The extreme cases of risk allocation are the priced options A and B, on the one hand and the cost reimbursable option E on the other hand. In the priced options, the *Contractor* is paid for work at tendered prices. He carries all risks other than the *Employer*'s risks stated in the contract and the financial and time effects of compensation events. In a cost reimbursable contract, the *Contractor* is paid his properly expended costs. The target options C and D, permit the cost risk to be shared between the *Employer* and the *Contractor*. The management option F is essentially cost reimbursable but risk allocation can be varied by choosing appropriate main options in the subcontracts.

The priced and target options include a choice between two types of pricing document, namely an *activity schedule* and a *bill of quantities*.

This range of choice covers most arrangements used in all types of engineering and building construction. Construction management, in which the *Contractor* provides management services to the *Employer* but has no responsibility for construction work, is also provided for. In this case the *Employer* appoints a construction management contractor as *Project Manager*. He then advises the *Employer* on placing trade or construction contracts using one of the main options for each contract.

For a particular contract, one main option must be chosen. The optional clauses are combined with the core clauses to provide a complete contract. The core clauses cannot be used on their own. They are clauses which are common to the types of contract covered by the main options.

The following are brief summaries of the main characteristics and uses of each main option. Further notes on the preparation of the various documents are given under 'Tender Documents'. Further explanation is given in the Explanatory Notes for Sections 5 and 6.

Option A: Priced contract with activity schedule

An *activity schedule* is a list of activities prepared by the *Contractor* which he expects to carry out in Providing the Works. When it has been priced by the *Contractor*, the lump sum for each activity is the Price to be paid by the *Employer* for that activity. The total of these Prices is the *Contractor*'s price for providing the whole of the *works* including for all matters which are at the *Contractor*'s risk. Option A provides for stage payments (see notes under 'Tender Documents').

Option B: Priced contract with bill of quantities

A *bill of quantities* comprises a list of work items and quantities. Standard methods of measurement are published which state the items to be included and how the quantities are to be calculated. Tenderers price the items, taking account of the information in the tender documents and including for all matters which are at the *Contractor*'s risk.

Options C and D: Target contracts (with activity schedule or bill of quantities)

Target contracts are sometimes used where the extent of work to be done is not fully defined or where anticipated risks are greater. The financial risk is shared between the *Employer* and the *Contractor* in the following way:

- The *Contractor* tenders a target price in the form of the Prices using either an *activity schedule* or a *bill of quantities*. The target price includes the *Contractor*'s estimate of Actual Cost plus other costs, overheads and profit to be covered by his Fee.
- The *Contractor* tenders his Fee in terms of a *fee percentage* to be applied to Actual Cost.
- During the course of the contract, the *Contractor* is paid Actual Cost plus the Fee. This is defined as the Price for Work Done to Date (PWDD) (see notes on Section 5). The Prices are adjusted for the effects of compensation events and for inflation if Option N is used.
- At the end of the contract, the *Contractor* is paid (or pays) his share of the difference between the final total of the Prices and the final PWDD according to a formula stated in the Contract Data. If the final PWDD is greater than the final total of the Prices, the *Contractor* pays his share of the difference. The *Contractor*'s share is paid provisionally at Completion and is corrected in the final account.

(See further notes on Clause 53.)

Option E: Cost reimbursable contract

A cost reimbursable contract should be used when the definition of the work to be done is inadequate even as a basis for a target price and yet an early start to construction is required. In such circumstances, the *Contractor* cannot be expected to take cost risks other than those which entail control of his employees and other resources. He carries minimum risk and is paid Actual Cost plus his tendered Fee, subject only to a small number of constraints designed to motivate efficient working.

Option F: Management contract

The conditions of contract applied to management contracts are still evolving. In practice there are several different approaches used in relation to, for example, scope of services, time of appointment and methods of fee payment. The terms under which subcontractors are employed are also changing. The ECC management contract is based on the following framework.

The *Contractor*'s responsibilities for construction work are the same as those taken by a contractor working under the other main options although he does not carry out any construction himself. The *Contractor*'s services apply mainly to the construction phase although he would usually be appointed before construction starts. If substantial pre-construction services are required and the *Employer* wishes to have the option to change the Management Contractor before construction starts, a separate contract should be awarded for a pre-construction service contract, using the NEC Professional Services Contract.

All subcontracts are direct contracts with the Management Contractor. If the *Employer* wishes to be a party to the construction subcontracts a management contract is not appropriate. He should then appoint a construction manager as the *Project Manager* and use the ECC with appropriate main options for the contracts with package contractors.

The Management Contractor tenders his Fee and his estimated total of the prices of the subcontracts. The subcontract prices are paid to the Management Contractor as Actual Cost and are the only element paid in this way. The Management Contractor is responsible for supplying management services and completing design if required. In the latter case the contract becomes a design and management contract.

The Management Contractor's Fee will increase as Subcontractors' prices (Actual Cost to the Management Contractor) increase due to compensation events. However, he will not receive separate payment for his work in dealing with compensation events and he will not receive any additional Fee for work on compensation events which does not lead to an increase in Subcontractors' prices.

Options C, D, E and F

These options do not include the equivalent of Clause 63.10 in Options A and B. Therefore, both the Subcontractor's Fee and the Contractor's Fee should be included in the assessment of a compensation event.

The secondary options

After deciding the main option, the user may choose any of the secondary options. It is not necessary to use any of them except that Option U must be used for UK contracts. The chosen secondary options, together with the chosen main option, must be identified in the first statement of part one of the Contract Data.The secondary options are

Option G	Performance bond
Option H	Parent company guarantee
Option J	Advanced payment to the *Contractor*
Option K	Multiple currencies (not to be used with Options C, D, E and F)
Option L	Sectional Completion
Option M	Limitation of the *Contractor*'s liability for his design to reasonable skill and care
Option N	Price adjustment for inflation (not to be used with Options E and F)
Option P	Retention (not to be used with Option F)
Option Q	Bonus for early Completion
Option R	Delay damages
Option S	Low performance damages
Option T	Changes in the law
Option U	The Construction (Design and Management) Regulations 1994 (to be used for contracts in the UK)
Option V	Trust Fund
Option Z	Additional conditions of contract

Choice of options

The sequence of decisions to be taken in choosing the main and secondary options for a particular contract are illustrated in Figure 2.

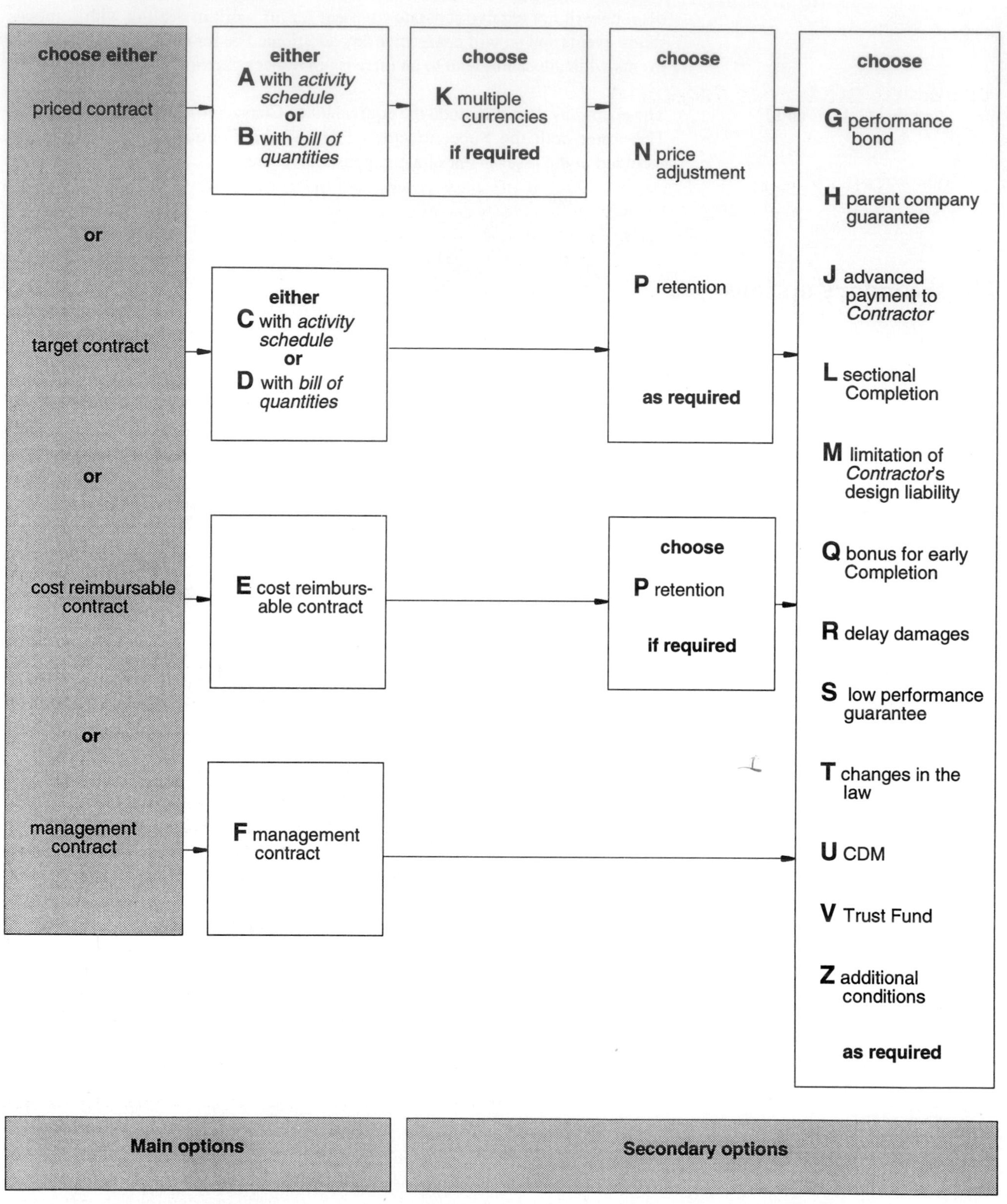

Figure 2. Options using the NEC Engineering and Construction Contract

TENDER DOCUMENTS

Preparing the tender documents

Deciding the contracts

Having decided the contract strategy, the *Employer* is able to decide which contracts he requires to carry out the project, what types of contract (choosing from the main options A to F in each case), how they relate to each other in time and physically and what secondary options he will use for each contract.

The tender documents

It is not necessary to issue the ECC printed documents to tenderers as they are incorporated by reference in the Contract Data. The documents to be issued with invitations to tender include

- instructions to tenderers (including any instructions for preparing activity schedules under Options A and C),
- a form of tender,
- Contract Data part one,
- Contract Data part two (pro-forma for completion by tenderers),
- bill of quantities (Options B and D),
- Works Information,
- Site Information,
- Health and Safety Plan (if Option U is used).

Form of tender

No standard form of tender has been included in the ECC, as many *Employers* have standard forms containing their own requirements. A suggested form is included in Appendix 2.

Contract Data

In the clauses of the ECC, the term Contract Data refers to the data which exist at the Contract Date. It may happen that the Contract Data part one issued to tenderers and the Contract Data part two which is completed and returned by a tenderer as part of his offer are changed during negotiations between the *Employer* and the potential *Contractor*. The Contract Data define the details of the agreement which is in the contract. The conditions of contract make provision for certain changes such as replacement of key people, change of *completion date* and replacement of the *Adjudicator*.

The purpose of the Contract Data is to provide data as required by the *conditions of contract* specific to a particular contract. The terms in italics in the *conditions of contract* must be identified in the Contract Data in accordance with Clause 11.1. The Contract Data is a key document in any contract using the ECC.

The format for both parts one and two of the Contract Data for a particular contract enquiry should be assembled by the *Employer* using the formats and wording for each statement as set out in the ECC with spaces adjusted appropriately. As well as the statements to be given in all contracts, the selected optional statements should be included (preferably within the statements for the relevant Section of the ECC) but omitting the explanatory sentences printed in bold type and commencing 'If........' which are only for the guidance of users. The statements in part two of the Contract Data about Data for Schedule of Cost Components (SCC) should be included in all contracts except when Option F is used.

In order to avoid lengthy entries for certain statements, it may be convenient to list them in a separate document which is clearly referenced in the Contract Data.

For example, a schedule of drawings could be referred to in the Contract Data rather than reproducing it in full.

Part one

This is completed by the *Employer* for each contract. Worked examples are given in Appendix 5.

The opening statement in '1. General' identifies the clauses in the conditions of contract for a particular contract.

Part two

This part contains a list of data to be supplied by tenderers as part of their offer. Certain information is to be given in all contracts.

Optional statements follow from which the *Employer* will have selected those he requires. For instance, the statement regarding the *completion date* should be included only if the *Employer* has not fixed the *completion date* in the Contract Data part one and wishes tenderers to submit their proposals.

The tendered total of the Prices must be entered where Option A, B, C or D is used. This will be transferred from the grand total of the *activity schedule* or *bill of quantities* as the case may be. In assessing tenders, it is most important that the total entered in the Contract Data is checked against the total of the *activity schedule* or *bill of quantities*.

The data for the Schedule of Cost Components comprise information to be tendered relating to calculation of Actual Cost. This is required to assess compensation events (Options A to E) and to calculate payments due to the *Contractor* in Options C, D and E. The cost component data for use with the Shorter Schedule of Cost Components, which are also part of a *Contractor*'s tender, can only be used for assessing compensation events.

The information submitted by tenderers in part two of the Contract Data is used in assessing tenders. For *works* which fall within European Community legislation, the publication of award criteria is a requirement of the procurement directive.

One of the most important figures tendered is the *fee percentage*. When Options A, B, C or D are used, a provisional amount multiplied by the tendered fee percentage should be included in the forecast final price when comparing tenders. See further notes under 'Assessing Tenders'. In this way, the quoted fee is made part of the competition for the work. If this is not done, *Employers* run a risk of receiving tenders with inflated fee percentages. In Options E and F the *fee percentage* tendered is the main factor in the financial assessment of tenders.

Activity schedule
General use with Options A and C

This document is prepared and priced by tenderers. Its use varies between Options A and C. It is not part of the Works Information and must not be used to describe the *works*.

The prices entered by the tenderers for each activity are lump sums, not unit rates as in a *bill of quantities*. The tenderer decides how to break up his work into activities, enters them on the schedule and prices each one. If the *Employer* wants to specify particular activities which the *Contractor* is to identify in the *activity schedule* he may do so, stating his requirements in the instructions to tenderers.

Use of Options A and C of the ECC does not require a bill of quantities to be issued to tenderers or to be used subsequently. Consequently, tenderers have to calculate quantities from the Works Information where they need to know a quantity in order to estimate the cost of the work. For many contracts (including process plant, building construction etc) this is a significant task.

In order to reduce the cost and time involved during the bid preparation period, *Employers* may wish to calculate quantities before inviting tenders and then issue a copy of the quantities list to all tenderers. When this is done, it must be made clear that the tenderer will have used the quantities and relied upon them entirely at his own risk of their inaccuracy or incompleteness. No amendment to the contract or addition to the contract is necessary to achieve this as the contract is clear that the *Contractor*'s obligation is to carry out the work described in the Works Information. There is no mechanism for this obligation to be qualified or modified by the issue of quantities to tenderers. The same considerations apply to the issue of quantities to tendering subcontractors when the ECS is used.

Use with Option A

A contract which uses Option A is a lump sum contract with the *activity schedule* showing a breakdown of the total lump sum.

The total of the prices of the items in the *activity schedule* is the tenderer's offer for Providing the Works. The cost of any items the tenderer may have omitted is deemed to be included in the prices for the other items. There is provision in the conditions for adjusting the *activity schedule* for compensation events and for changes in a planned method of working (see Clauses 63.8 and 54.2). The only other way of changing the *activity schedule* is if the *Project Manager* accepts a quotation for acceleration (Clause 36.3).

The *activity schedule* should include activities such as design tasks and erecting temporary works.

There is no provision for payment for Equipment or Plant and Materials within the Working Areas before they are incorporated into the *works* i.e. equivalent to 'materials on site'. The *Contractor* may wish to receive earlier payment to improve his cash flow. The required effect can be obtained under option A by including appropriate items in the *activity schedule*. The special circumstances under which payment might be made for Equipment or Plant and Materials which are outside the Working Areas are covered in Section 7.

If no grouping of activities is included, the *Contractor* is paid for each activity when it is completed (see Clause 11.2(24)).

Stage payments using Option A

If a group of activities is defined in the *activity schedule*, the *Contractor* is paid for the activities included in it when the whole group is completed. This is how the ECC provides for stage payments. At each payment assessment date the state of completion of each group of activities is assessed. Only the prices of completed groups are included in the amount due (see further notes on Clause 50).

The groups of activities should correspond with easily identified stages of the work, e.g. for a building: site preparation, excavation, piling, foundations, structural frame (by floors), floors, cladding, partitions, roof, finishes.

If stage payments for a manufacturer's design, manufacture and installation of a large item of Plant are intended, the instructions to tenderers could state that the *activity schedule* should include the groups of activities necessary to complete stages such as:

- confirm acceptance of order by manufacturer,
- acceptance of design,
- stages in the shop assembly of components,
- delivery to Site,
- provision of vendor data and
- acceptance of performance tests by the *Supervisor*.

Option A Instructions to tenderers

The following text should be included in instructions to tenderers for Option A enquiries:

Activity Schedule

Tenderers are to submit an activity schedule with their tenders. This will be a document headed 'Activity Schedule' and will comprise a list of activities with an amount entered against each activity. This amount is the sum due to the *Contractor* on completion of each activity unless it is included in a group. If groups of activities are required to be identified on the schedule, payment for each group becomes due when all the activities in that group are completed.

Activity descriptions must be clear and complete so that the work included in each can be identified.

The following activities must be included in the schedule but may be subdivided:

[List of particular activities to be identified.]

The following groups of activities must be identified in the schedule.

[List of groups of activities to be identified.]

Use with Option C

Because of the nature of target contracts it is recommended that an *activity schedule* is normally used to determine the target price (the Prices), rather than a *bill of quantities*. The above notes on *activity schedules* in Option A apply except that there is little point in requiring groups of activities to be identified because the *activity schedule* in Option C is not used directly for payment purposes. However, it is used to adjust the Prices when compensation events occur and subsequently for calculating the *Contractor*'s share after Completion (see Clause 53).

Bill of quantities
General use with Options C and D

The *method of measurement*, on which the *bill of quantities* is based, is identified in part one of the Contract Data. This should also include identification of any amendments or additions to the standard *method of measurement*.

The *bill of quantities* is to be priced and extended by tenderers, to produce the tendered total of the Prices.

There is no provision for payment for Equipment or Plant and Materials within the Working Areas before they are incorporated into the *works*, i.e. equivalent to 'materials on site'. The *Contractor* may wish to receive earlier payment to improve his cash flow. The required effect can be obtained under option B by inserting appropriate items in the Method Related Charges where the method of measurement allows or, alternatively, making allowance in the rates of the *bill of quantities* for the financing of the Equipment or Plant and Materials until they are incorporated in the *works*. The special circumstances under which payment might be made for Equipment or Plant and Materials which are outside the Working Areas are covered in Section 7.

It is important that the *bill of quantities* should be prepared to suit the position at which the boundary between the *Employer*'s and the *Contractor*'s design is set for each contract. All the standard methods of measurement which are available assume that the *Employer* is responsible for most of the design. The rules for itemisation and description of the work are set accordingly.

Consequently, when using ECC with the *Contractor* carrying out more design, the existing methods of measurement must be amended or a special method of measurement substituted. In extreme cases, such as when the *Contractor* is carrying out most of the design, the activity schedule options A and C of the ECC should be used.

For example, standard methods of measurement usually require separate items to be given for concrete, reinforcement and formwork in reinforced concrete with quantities for each. When the *Contractor* is to design the reinforced concrete, it is impossible to calculate the quantities before he is appointed. It is also contractually wrong as the *Contractor* takes the risk of quantity variation for items which he has designed. The principle which must be followed is that the items in the *bill of quantities* must not describe the work using any assumptions about what the *Contractor* may choose to provide or about the quantities of work which he will choose to provide.

Tender document in cost reimbursable contracts General use with Options E and F

If the *Contractor* for a cost reimbursable contract is selected by competitive tendering, the basis on which tenders are selected should be clearly stated in the invitation to tender. Award criteria will include the level of the *fee percentage* tendered and the various percentages tendered as cost component data. For this purpose, provisional estimates of Actual Cost should be included in a tender document together with provisional amounts to which the various tendered percentages in the cost component data are applied. This will provide a notional tender price on which tenders can be assessed.

Works Information

The documents containing the Works Information provided by the *Employer* are identified in part one of the Contract Data. Any Works Information for the *Contractor*'s design submitted by tenderers with their tenders is to be identified in part two of the Contract Data. Most of this information will be given in a specification and on drawings in the traditional manner. Where information is provided by non-documentary means such as models, they should be identified and their availability and location stated.

The Works Information in part one of the Contract Data should include the following items. The related contract clause numbers are given in brackets.

Description of *works*

- A general description of the works including general arrangement and location drawings.
- Working/production and other detailed drawings, specification, models and other means used to describe the parts of the works designed by the Employer.
- A statement of any constraints on how the Contractor Provides the Works eg restrictions on access, sequences of construction.

Plant and Materials

- Materials and workmanship specifications.
- Requirements for delivery and storage before their incorporation of Plant and Materials in the works, provision of spares and the specification of the vendor data required. This can conveniently be included in the specification.

Health and safety [18.1]

The particular health and safety requirements, such as the safety regulations for the factory within which the Site is located. Any health and safety plan for the project, as may be required by statute, should also be included.

Contractor's design [21.1]

A statement of those parts of the works which the Contractor is to design. The form of this statement will depend on the extent of the Contractor's design responsibility. For contracts with little *Contractor*'s design, a list of what is left to be designed by the *Contractor* should be provided. For more comprehensive design and construct contracts, a list of what has been designed by the *Employer* should be given, with the *Contractor* being made responsible for designing the remainder.

	[21.2]	A design brief or performance specification for those parts of the *works* to be designed by the *Contractor,* including • size or space limitations, • design standards and codes of practice, • materials and workmanship specifications including references to relevant standards, • loading and capacity requirements, • operational performance requirements and design life.
	[21.2]	Procedures which the *Contractor* is to follow in carrying out his design. Particulars of the design which are to be submitted to the *Project Manager*, including requirements for certification and/or checking.
	[22.1]	The purposes for which the *Employer* may require to use and copy the *Contractor*'s design.
Completion	[11.2 (13)]	The work required to be done by the *completion date* for the whole of the *works* and, if Option L is used, for each of the *sections*. Alternatively, this could be in the form of a list of work which can remain undone at the *completion date*.
Services	[25.1]	Details of other contractors and Others who will be occupying the Working Areas during the contract period indicating which parts they will occupy, and for what periods.
	[33.2]	The facilities and services which the *Employer* and the *Contractor* are to provide to each other and to others whilst the *Contractor* has possession of the Site.
Subcontracting	[26]	• Lists of acceptable subcontractors for particular tasks. • Statement of any work which should not be subcontracted. • Statement of any work which is required to be subcontracted.
Programme	[31.3]	Any information which the *Contractor* is required to include in the programme in addition to that stated in clause 31.2. On multi-contract projects, it will probably be necessary for the *Contractor* to provide boundary data, foundation design data, 'hook-up' data and similar information relating to his design for the use of the *Employer* and other contractors. The times when this information is to be submitted should be stated in accordance with the overall programme for the project. Provision of this information should be a separate activity identified in the programme.
Tests	[40.1]	Description of the tests to be carried out by the *Contractor*, the *Supervisor* and others including those which must be done before Completion.
	[40.2]	Specification of materials, facilities and samples to be provided by the *Contractor* and by the *Employer* for tests.
	[41.1]	Specification of Plant and Materials which are to be inspected or tested before delivery to the Working Areas including details of the inspection or test.
	[71.1]	Definition of tests of Plant and Materials outside the Working Areas which have to be passed before marking by the *Supervisor*.
Title	[73.2]	Statement of any materials from excavation and demolition to which the *Contractor* will have title.
Damage to highways, etc.		No equivalent to Clause 30 of the ICE Conditions of Contract is included as this is a special case of third party damage which is covered in section 8.

If Option C, D or E is used

Acceptance or procurement procedures [11.2 (30)] The acceptance or procurement procedures to be followed by the *Contractor*.

If Option C, D, E or F is used

Accounts and records [52.2] Details of accounts and records to be kept by the *Contractor* other than those already stated in Clause 52.2.

If Option F is used

Subcontracts [20.2] Details of work to be subcontracted.

If Option G is used

Performance bond [G1.1] The form of the performance bond.

If Option H is used

Parent company guarantee [H1.1] The form of the guarantcc.

If Option J is used

Advanced payment bond [J1.2] The form of the advanced payment bond (if required in the Contract Data).

If Option S is used

Performance test [S1.1] Details of any test to be used to measure the performance of the *works* or an item of Plant for which low performance damages are specified.

Site Information

The documents in which the Site Information is contained are identified in part one of the Contract Data. Site Information may include the following:

- Subsoil investigation borehole records and test results.
- Reports obtained by the *Employer* concerning the physical conditions within the Site or its surroundings. This may include mapping, hydrographic data, and hydrological information.
- References to publicly available information about the Site and its surroundings such as published papers and interpretations of the Geological Survey. The purpose of listing these references is to help a tenderer to prepare his tender and to decide his method of working and programme. Normally only factual information about physical conditions on the Site and its surroundings is included in the Site Information. Interpretation is a matter for the *Contractor*. However, some *Employers* may wish to include interpretative information, such as inferred geological sections.
- Information about plant and services below the surface of the Site.
- Information about piped and other services.
- Information about buildings, structures, plant (including machinery) adjacent to and on the Site.

Inviting and preparing tenders

Instructions to tenderers

When it is intended that the *Contractor* will carry out design work, the *Employer* may wish tendering contractors to submit information about their proposed design with their tenders. It is then included in part two of the Contract Data. If they do, the instructions to tenderers must include particulars of the information required. It is not essential to ask for any such information as the provisions of the ECC are designed so that the contract obligations and procedures are unaffected by the amount of pre-tender design carried out by tenderers. In any event, no more pre-tender design than is regarded by the *Employer* as essential should be asked for because, for all but one of the tenderers, the work will be abortive and an unrecovered cost. All tenderers will, of course, carry out such pre-tender design work as they decide is necessary to calculate their tendered prices.

The instructions to tenderers must also state which management functions are to be covered by the people who are to be identified in the Contract Data as key people.

The documents which tenderers will be required to submit will depend on which of the main options A to F and of the secondary options have been incorporated. In all cases, a complete form of tender will be required together with part two of the Contract Data. A suggested form of tender is included in Appendix 2.

Part two of the Contract Data

The statements to be given by the tenderer in all contracts are

- Name and address of the *Contractor*.
- The *fee percentage*. (ref. Clause 11.2(17))
  This is a tendered figure and will be taken into account in tender assessment (see later notes).
- Any area outside the Site which the *Contractor* proposes to use as a *working area*, should be identified.
- Key people.
  A list of names, job descriptions, responsibilities, qualifications and experience of key people is required. The *Employer* should indicate in the instructions to tenderers for whom in the tenderer's organisation these details are required. The *Contractor* has no incentive to insert details of more than the minimum number of key people since each stated name and position constrains him. Sometimes these details are finalised during pre-contract negotiations between *Employer* and *Contractor*.
- The Works Information for the *Contractor*'s design.
  If the *Contractor* is not required to carry out any design or if the *Employer* does not wish the *Contractor* to submit any pre-tender design, there will be no entry under this heading. Where the *Contractor* is required to submit a large part of the design, the entry will comprise a list of drawings and specifications accompanying the tender. It is neither necessary nor desirable to require full working drawings in most cases, but the submission should be sufficient to enable the *Employer* to assess the design which each tenderer is offering.

Further statements will depend on which options apply to the contract, and what information the *Employer* requires to be submitted with the tenders. These may include the following.

Programme

The programme reference number or title should be given and the programme submitted as a separate document. The main purpose of requiring submission of a programme with each tender is to inform the *Employer* of how the tenderer proposes to carry out the work and how it affects the *Employer*'s other contracts and activities.

Completion date

If a *completion date* is to be proposed by the tenderer this should be stated in the Contract Data part two having been calculated from the *starting date* and taking account of the *possession dates* stated by the *Employer* in the Contract Data part one.

Activity schedule (Options A and C)

A reference number or title should be given and the schedule submitted as a separate document. The *Employer* should state in the instructions to tenderers any activities or groups of activities he requires to be included.

Bill of quantities (Options B and D)

The *Contractor* enters a reference to the priced *bill of quantities* which is being included in his tender.

Tendered total of Prices

For priced and target contracts (Options A, B, C, and D), the tendered total should be entered. This will comprise the total of the *bill of quantities* or *activity schedule* as the case may be. The total of a *bill of quantities* will be subject to remeasurement and correction in accordance with the *method of measurement*. In the event of any discrepancy between the total of the *bill of quantities* or the *activity schedule* and the total entered in the Contract Data, it should be made clear to tenderers which of the totals has priority. The instruction to tenderers should also state how arithmetical errors are to be corrected.

Data for Schedule of Cost Components

For all main options other than the management contract (Option F), the details under this heading, as well as the data using the shorter schedule are entered by the tenderers. The percentages entered are not equivalent to the dayworks percentages in a conventional contract. (See notes on the Schedule of Cost Components.)

Assessing tenders

Award criteria

To ensure equal treatment of all tenderers and to assist in their understanding of the *Employer*'s requirements, the criteria upon which tenders are to be assessed, and the weight given to the various tendered elements, should be clearly stated in the instructions to tenderers. These criteria can be in the form of a 'Tender Assessment Sheet'. An example of such a sheet suitable for use with Options A and B is given in Appendix 4.

Procurement law

If the contract is subject to procurement legislation, there may be a requirement to assess tenders on the basis of objective criteria made available to all tenderers. All relevant criteria should therefore be published, as it may infringe the law if other criteria, however commercially or technically desirable are used to select the *Contractor*.

General law

In some jurisdictions, publication of assessment criteria may create an implied requirement that the published criteria must be followed by the Employer. Thus even if specific procurement legislation does not apply, all relevant factors should be stated, including those not readily quantifiable such as aesthetic considerations.

Contractor's design

It is most important that all documents submitted with tenders are carefully examined as, once accepted, a tender becomes contractually binding on both Parties. The only exception to this is any design by the *Contractor* (submitted in part two of the Contract Data). Where any part of this design does not comply with the Works Information in part one of the Contract Data (the *Employer*'s requirements), the latter has precedence. The *Employer* should check the *Contractor*'s design proposals carefully, as many aspects may not be covered by the criteria specified by the *Employer* in the Works Information in part one of the Contract Data.

Arithmetical checks

It is essential to carry out arithmetical checks of the *bills of quantities* and *activity schedules*. Any corrections should be made in accordance with the instructions to tenderers, and agreed and signed by both Parties before a tender is accepted.

Overall assessment

In order to assess tenders, the *Employer* should apply the quantitative information entered by the tenderers in part two of the Contract Data, to provisional amounts previously entered by the *Employer*, in a systematic way. The resulting total should then be considered together with the tendered total of the Prices (for Options A, B, C and D) and any other relevant matters, to decide to whom the contract should be awarded.

A model tender assessment sheet suitable for use with Options A and B is given in Appendix 4. All items may not be required for a particular contract. Items should be selected as required. The assessment sheet should be issued to tenderers for their information with the invitation to tender. Although it is suggested that estimates of final costs used to decide assessment criteria should be based on historical data, neither *Employers* nor tenderers should assume that this is the expected outturn or the *Employer*'s contract contingency.

The notes included in Appendix 4 apply to the numbered items on the sheet, and give guidance on the figures to be inserted by the *Employer* before the sheet is issued to tenderers.

Creating the contract

Frequently, negotiations with one or more tenderers are necessary to clarify intentions, to agree amendments, to eliminate qualifications which are not acceptable to the *Employer* and to discuss the *Contractor*'s design. It is important to minimise these negotiations since extended discussions can result in abuse of the tendering process. This can be achieved by careful preparation of tender documents and instructions to tenderers and by stating award criteria in objective terms.

The creation of a contract can be by means of acceptance of a tender or a revised tender or by means of acceptance by the *Contractor* of a counter-offer prepared by or on behalf of the *Employer*. A binding contract is thus created, although some *Employers* may require such acceptance being subject to a formal agreement. A suitable form of agreement is included in Appendix 3 but *Employers* often have their own standard forms. Essentially they record the agreement between the two Parties and identify the documents which make up the contract.

EXPLANATORY NOTES

1 General

CORE CLAUSES

Actions 10

10.1 This clause obliges the *Employer*, the *Contractor*, the *Project Manager* and the *Supervisor* to do everything which the contract states they do. It is the only clause which uses the future tense. For simplicity, everything else is in the present tense.

The requirement for the principal contributors to the operation of an ECC contract to do so in a spirit of mutual trust and co-operation was added on the recommendation of the Latham Report ('Constructing the Team'). This report, published in July 1994, was the final report of an investigation by Sir Michael Latham into procurement and contractual arrangements in the UK construction industry. The ECC takes account of all the recommendations of the Latham Report.

Where actions are permitted but not obligatory, the term 'may' is used.

Identified and defined terms 11

11.1 The main definitions used in the contract are given in this clause. Other definitions are given in optional clauses where they are specific to a particular option. Capital initial letters are used in the ECC for the terms defined to distinguish them from undefined terms. The same conventions for italics and capital initials are used in these guidance notes as in the ECC itself.

11.2 (2) The defined term 'Others' provides a convenient means of reference to people and organisations not directly involved in the contract. However, there are instances where it is not appropriate to exclude some of the exceptions, e.g. in Clause 16.2. In these cases the term 'other people' is used to avoid any impression of a typing error which might have been given if 'others' were to be used without the capital initial.

(3) Contracts come into existence by various means – sometimes by means of a counter-offer and its acceptance, sometimes after extended negotiations and discussions. The Contract Date is used to define the date when the contract comes into existence, regardless of the means by which this is achieved.

It is very important to establish and document the means by which the contract came into existence and the date on which it came into existence. If this is not done, there is a significant risk of later difficulties if a dispute about the contract arises. (See also earlier notes on 'Creating the contract'.)

(5) Works Information is information about the *works* to be provided. Detailed guidance on assembling the Works Information is given under 'Preparing the tender documents'. Works Information can be varied by the *Project Manager* during the course of the contract (Clause 14.3).

(6) Site Information includes information about the surroundings of the Site. Detailed guidance on assembling the Site Information is given under 'Preparing the tender documents'.

(7) The *boundaries of the site* will normally be shown on a drawing which is identified in part one of the Contract Data.

(8) The *Contractor* may state in part two of the Contract Data any additional *working areas* he proposes to use. These will include any areas of land which he proposes to use temporarily for the purposes of the contract. They can be added to during the course of the contract, provided they are accepted by the *Project Manager*, as set out in Clause 15.

(9) This definition of a Subcontractor does not include a supplier to the *Contractor* except as stated in the clause.

(10) Items temporarily used in the construction but removed at or before Completion are excluded from Plant and Materials.

(11) The definition of Equipment is broad and avoids using separate terms for items which are treated in the same way under the contract. It covers, for example, construction plant, vehicles, consumables, tools, temporary works, cabins, temporary access roads and other site facilities. The term 'Equipment' has been used where it has been customary to use 'plant' or 'constructional plant' in UK building and (until recently) civil engineering practice. This change is made so that the ECC can be used internationally and for other engineering work where it is customary for 'the plant' to mean part of the *works* to be provided.

Normally Equipment is eventually removed from the Site but there is provision in clause 72 for the *Project Manager* to give approval for certain items to be left. For example, the *Contractor* may request that temporary piling should be left in, to save the cost of extraction. Also, the *Project Manager* may be content to permit 'sacrificial' formwork to be left in place.

(12) The *completion date* stated in the Contract Data may be changed in various ways, for example, as a consequence of a compensation event or of an agreement to accelerate.

(13) The Works Information must state what work is to be done before Completion. This provides flexibility for the *Employer* to specify Completion at the level he requires and largely avoids the uncertainty associated with terms such as 'substantial completion' or 'partial completion'. Where normal practice is to equate completion with absolute completion, as in some Middle Eastern countries, the Works Information will be written so that work must be free of Defects before Completion.

(14) The definition of the Accepted Programme is worded to allow for the two situations where there may or may not have been a requirement for tenderers to submit a programme with their tenders. A tender programme is identified in the Contract Data and becomes the Accepted Programme when the contract comes into existence.

(15) The word 'Defect' has a restricted definition. It excludes faults in work caused by faulty design for which the *Employer* is responsible.

(16) Issue of the Defects Certificate signifies the end of most of the obligations of the Parties. Uncorrected Defects listed in the Defects Certificate are dealt with using the procedure set out in clause 45.

(17) Any costs of the *Contractor* not included in the defined Actual Cost are deemed to be included, together with profit, in the Fee (Clause 52.1). The *fee percentage* is stated by each tenderer in part two of the Contract Data. It is then applied to the Actual Cost of work already done and the forecast Actual Cost of work not yet done in assessing compensation events. In Options C, D E and F, it is also used to calculate payments to the *Contractor*. (See also notes on Schedule of Cost Components.)

(18) Not used in ECC 2nd edition.

Communications 13

13.1 The phrase 'in a form which can be read, copied and recorded' includes a document sent by post, telex, cable, electronic mail, facsimile transmission, and on disc, magnetic tape or other electronic means.

13.3
13.4 These clauses establish the use of a *period for reply* wherever the term (identified in the Contract Data part one) is used in the *conditions of contract*.

13.5 This clause provides for extending the *period for reply* by agreement. Where other periods for action are stated in the ECC, provisions for their extension (if any) are stated in the relevant clauses.

A similar clause is included in the EC Subcontract. The *Contractor* should not agree to extend the *period for reply* for a subcontract unless he has obtained the *Project Manager*'s agreement to an appropriate extension for the main contract.

13.7 The requirement to notify information required by the contract separately is included to avoid important things being missed. For example, so that delays which could be avoided are not missed, submission of a revised programme which shows a delay does not count as an early warning of the delay.

13.8 The ECC contains a number of examples of situations in which a *Project Manager* must either accept or reject a document which contains proposals submitted by the *Contractor*. The first example is in Clause 13.4. As Clause 13.8 says, the *Project Manager* may withhold acceptance of a submission although it is clearly not sensible for him to withhold acceptance for a reason which has no bearing on the interests on the *Employer*. However, some of these reasons may be quite outside the influence of the *Contractor* or may arise due to factors which the *Contractor* had no means of foreseeing. The mechanism described in Clause 13.8 is introduced to limit the *Contractor*'s risk in this situation. He does carry the risk of the *Project Manager* withholding acceptance for a reason stated in the contract. Withholding acceptance for any other reason is a compensation event (Clause 60.1(9)). This arrangement gives the *Project Manager* freedom to withhold acceptance for any reasons but limits the *Contractor*'s risk associated with this freedom.

The *Project Manager* and the Supervisor 14

14.1 The *Project Manager* is the key person involved in the management of the contract from the *Employer*'s point of view. His duties and authority are described in the clauses of the contract. They are not summarised in a single clause.

It is assumed that the *Project Manager* will confer with the *Employer* as necessary in deciding which of various possible actions to take and in making other decisions which affect the outcome of the project as far as the *Employer* is concerned. For example, the *Project Manager* has full authority to arrange an acceleration of work, although the *Employer* would normally be vitally interested. The fact that the *Employer* is not often mentioned in the contract does not mean that the *Employer* has only a minor role. It does mean that, for the purposes of the contract, almost all dealings with the *Contractor* are handled by the *Project Manager*.

The *Project Manager* should advise the *Employer* whenever he sees fit, or when his conditions of engagement require, of any action which the *Project Manager* is considering. For example, the *Project Manager* may inform the *Employer* of acceptable quotations for compensation events, and also consult with him on which alternative quotation most suits the *Employer*'s requirements.

The *Contractor* will expect that all decisions which the contract envisages will be taken by the *Project Manager* will be taken by him and that he will take them within the time limits stated in the contract. In some organisations, this may require the *Project Manager* to pass on decisions to the *Contractor* which have in fact been taken by the *Employer*. This may happen, for example, when an *Employer* has not delegated the authority to make a particular type of decision to his *Project*

Manager. This creates no difficulty provided that the internal arrangements between the *Employer* and the *Project Manager* enable the decisions to be made and communicated to the *Contractor* through the *Project Manager* within the contractual time limits.

The *Supervisor* will normally be appointed by the *Employer*. His main function is to check that work is carried out in compliance with the Works Information. This may include testing of materials and workmanship and observing tests which the *Contractor* carries out. He is also concerned with identifying and correcting Defects and, eventually, certifying the remaining Defects when he issues the Defects Certificate. His activities may have financial consequences, but he is not directly involved in financial matters. The actions of the *Project Manager* and *Supervisor* are independent of each other. There is no appeal from the *Supervisor* to the *Project Manager* where the actions of the *Supervisor* are questioned by the *Contractor*. If the *Contractor* is dissatisfied with an action of either the *Project Manager* or the *Supervisor*, his appeal is to the *Adjudicator*. (See also notes in 'Introduction'.)

14.2 On major contracts, it is normal for both the *Project Manager* and *Supervisor* to have staff to help them carry out their duties. This clause enables them to delegate specific authorities and duties under the contract to particular members of staff or others. Before delegation is effective, the *Contractor* must first be notified. Notification of the *Contractor* should include details of the actions delegated and the person to whom they are delegated.

Delegation does not prevent the person who delegates from also acting himself. The *Project Manager* would normally advise the *Employer* and the *Supervisor*, as well as the *Contractor* of any delegation of his actions, but this is entirely a matter for arrangement between these parties. In the same way the *Supervisor* would normally inform the *Project Manager* and the *Employer* of any delegation of his actions. A *Project Manager* will not normally delegate actions to the *Supervisor*, or the other way round. However, in very small contracts, where for example the *Supervisor* is absent for unavoidable reasons, it may be convenient for him to delegate his actions to the *Project Manager*.

14.3 The authority to change the Works Information belongs exclusively to the *Project Manager* and any person to whom he delegates this authority. Neither the *Employer* nor the *Supervisor* can change the Works Information. The *Adjudicator* cannot change the Works Information. The ECC does not limit the ordinary meaning of the word 'change' in relation to a change to the Works Information. Consequently, it includes additions to and deletions from the Works Information as well as alterations to it. If, for example, the *Project Manager* issues new information which he intends merely to clarify a previously issued drawing or specification clause this is as much a change to the Works Information as the issue of a new drawing which adds to the work which the *Contractor* has to do. Consequently, all such changes are potentially compensation events as set out in Clause 60.1(1).

Adding to the *working areas* **15**

15.1 This clause does not prevent the *Project Manager* and the *Contractor* agreeing to add a Working Area which is not going to be used solely for work on the contract. It provides that the *Project Manager* has no obligation to accept such a Working Area. The effects of identifying an area as a Working Area are set out in the clauses on title in Section 7 and in the Schedule of Cost Components.

Early warning **16**

16.1 The purpose of this clause is to make binding the obligation to warn as soon as possible of anything which may affect the cost, timing of Completion and quality of the *works*. The sanction for failure by the *Contractor* to give early warning is to reduce the payment due to him for a related compensation event (Clause 63.4).

The *Project Manager* is motivated to give early warning in order to maximise the time available to consider the problem with the *Contractor* and thereby to increase the likelihood of finding the best solution to meet the *Employer*'s interests.

16.2 This clause authorises the *Project Manager* or the *Contractor* to call an early warning meeting at any time to discuss any problems or potential problems of which notice has been given so that they can be dealt with in good time. Examples of such problems are

- discovery of unexpected ground conditions,
- potential delay in the supply of crucial materials or plant,
- potential delay caused by the work of public utilities or other contractors,
- effects of bad weather,
- failure by a subcontractor to perform and
- design problems.

It may be agreed that other people should attend according to the particular circumstances. For example, Subcontractors, suppliers, public utilities, local authority representatives or the *Employer* himself may need to attend. This is an example of where the defined term 'Others' (Clause 11.2(2)) would not have been appropriate.

16.3 The intention of the requirement for the *Contractor* and *Project Manager* to co-operate is to ensure, as far as possible, that actions are taken and decisions made which avoid or mitigate the effects of problems on cost, quality and time.

Ambiguities and inconsistencies 17

17.1 This clause is intended to ensure that action is taken as soon as possible to deal with ambiguities and inconsistencies which are noticed in the contract documents. There is no stated precedence of documents. The *Project Manager* has the responsibility of instructing resolution of an ambiguity problem or an inconsistency between whichever documents it may occur. An instruction to change the Works Information in order to resolve an ambiguity or inconsistency is a compensation event. Assessment is based on the 'contra proferentem' rule as expressed in Clause 63.7.

If an inconsistency becomes apparent between the Works Information provided by the *Employer* and a design which is part of the Works Information provided by the *Contractor* and included in part two of the Contract Data, the instruction would normally be to require the design to comply with the *Employer*'s Works Information. Such a change would not be a compensation event (Clause 60.1(1)).

Health and safety 18

18.1 In many countries there are laws which place considerable responsibilities upon employers, employees and others in relation to health and safety. In most European countries there is much legislation relating to health and safety on construction sites. This legislation is regularly being increased in scope. Generally the sanctions for non-compliance are criminal in nature as opposed to civil. It is not appropriate or necessary to reproduce or to summarise this legislation in contract documents. The various parties each have their obligations under statute and the general law.

It is necessary, however, to include in the contract any particular requirements which the *Employer* has. These requirements are stated in the Works Information since they affect how the *Contractor* is to Provide the Works and are in parallel with statutory obligations. These requirements may include such matters as

- a health and safety plan for the whole Site,
- submission of safety policies for information and
- which party is responsible for maintaining areas used by several contractors in a safe condition.

In 1995, the Construction (Design and Management) Regulations 1994 came in to force in the UK. They require construction projects to adopt a regime of health and safety management which includes many matters which might formerly have been covered by specific *Employers* requirements. Contracts in the UK using the ECC must include secondary option U which provides for compensation to the *Contractor* if the application of the regulations causes delay or additional or changed work which an experienced contractor could not reasonably have been expected to have foreseen.

Illegal and impossible requirements **19**

19.1 A change to the Works Information in order to resolve illegal or impossible Works Information is a compensation event (Clause 60.1(1)).

MAIN OPTION CLAUSES

Identified and defined terms **11**

11.2 All the main option clauses in Section 1 are definitions concerning payment and cost. Guidance on these is included in the notes on Section 5.

2 The *Contractor*'s main responsibilities

This section sets out the *Contractor*'s main responsibilities. Other sections deal with particular responsibilities appropriate to the section heading.

CORE CLAUSES

Providing the Works 20

20.1 This clause states the *Contractor*'s basic obligation. 'Provide the Works' is defined in Clause 11.2(4). It includes supplying all the necessary resources to achieve the end result including designing, fabricating, delivering to Site, erecting, constructing, installing, testing and making good Defects. The Works Information provided by the *Employer* should state everything which is intended concerning the work, including design work, which the *Contractor* is to do.

The *Contractor*'s design 21

The ECC is suitable both for use in traditional civil contracts where all permanent work is designed by or on behalf of the *Employer* and the *Contractor*'s obligation is limited to constructing the *works* and in design and construct contracts where the *Contractor* designs and builds the whole of the *works* in accordance with criteria specified by the *Employer*. Between these two limits, contracts will include some design done by the *Employer* and some by the *Contractor*. For instance, it is common for civil engineering and building works to be fully designed by or on behalf of the *Employer*, with mechanical and electrical plant designed by the *Contractor* to the performance requirements of the *Employer*.

Using Option F, the ECC is suitable for a design and management contract as well as for a design and construct contract.

21.1 Those parts of the *works* which the *Contractor* is required to design should be stated in the Works Information and the interfaces with those parts of the *works* designed by the *Employer* identified. This may be done by stating 'everything except the following' or 'the following'. It is not recommended that parts of an element of work should be designed by different parties as this may confuse liability in the event of defects occurring.

Where the *Contractor* is required to design a part of the *works*, the *Employer* should state in the Works Information the criteria to which he requires designs to conform. This may include details of the form, geometry and dimensions of the *works*, specifications, codes of practice, standards and environmental criteria. (See earlier notes on 'Preparing the tender documents'.)

Where the *Contractor* is to carry out most of the design, the criteria for his design will be in the form of a performance specification. This will describe the characteristics, nature and performance of the finished work and should include any limitations which the *Employer* wishes to impose upon appearance, durability, operating and maintenance cost, etc.

Any change to the allocation of design responsibility or change or addition to the design criteria in the Works Information in part one of the Contract Data constitutes a change to the Works Information and is a compensation event.

21.2 The procedures for submission by the *Contractor* of design particulars and acceptance by the *Project Manager* are set out in this clause. The time limits are those stated in Clause 13. They are intended to encourage prompt action by the parties so that delay can be avoided and the whole process properly managed.

Two reasons for not accepting the *Contractor*'s design are stated. The *Project Manager* is not obliged to refuse acceptance of the *Contractor*'s design which does not comply with the Works Information but, if he does accept such design, he should change the Works Information accordingly. As stated in Clause 60.1(1), such a change to the Works Information is not a compensation event.

Sometimes, the *Project Manager* will see in the design submitted by the *Contractor* characteristics which, if they had been foreseen, he would earlier have stated to have been unacceptable by including an appropriate constraint in the Works Information. In this situation, the *Project Manager* should add the constraint to the Works Information in order to justify his withholding of acceptance of the *Contractor*'s design. This change to the Works Information is a compensation event. This clause in the ECC ensures that the *Contractor* is protected from the risk of additional constraints on his design being introduced after his commitment to the Prices for the work has been made.

The final sentence is intended to prevent abortive work which would result if the *Contractor* began to manufacture or construct to a design which had not been accepted.

21.3 It is important that submissions by the *Contractor* are in packages which are capable of being properly assessed. For instance, a foundation design cannot be properly assessed without some details of the superstructure and any Plant to be supported.

21.4 Under this clause, the *Contractor* takes the risk of infringement of any patent, copyright, or other type of protected design which he incorporates or uses in his own design.

21.5 The *Contractor*'s liability for his design can be limited to an amount stated in the Contract Data. This liability can also be limited to 'reasonable skill and care' by inclusion of Option M. Without this option, the *Contractor*'s obligation is to design strictly in compliance with the Works Information.

The limited liability for the *Contractor*'s design has effect only after the Defects Certificate has been issued (Clause 43.2). This is because the *Contractor* has unlimited liability to correct Defects until that time. The cost of correcting any uncorrected Defects listed in the Defects Certificate is covered by Clause 45.1. The *Contractor*'s liability to compensate the *Employer* rather than to correct Defects comes into action only after the Defects Certificate has been issued. If it is intended that there should be no limit of the type referred to in this clause, the word 'unlimited' should be inserted in the appropriate place in the Contract Data.

The reference in this clause to the Defects Certificate ensures that any amounts which the *Contractor* may have to pay for delay damages (secondary option R) or low performance damages (secondary option S) do not reduce the amount of compensation for other liabilities for *Contractor*'s design which the *Contractor* may have.

Design of Equipment 23

23.1 This clause allows the *Project Manager* to accept the *Contractor*'s design of Equipment without affecting the *Contractor*'s responsibilities (Clause 14.1). The *Contractor* is still liable if, after having made the Equipment to details which have been accepted, it fails because it did not comply with the Works Information. The clause gives three criteria for design of the Equipment. Failure to comply gives the *Project Manager* the right, but not the obligation, to decline to accept the design.

Unlike Clause 21.2, which provides that the *Contractor* should not proceed until the *Project Manager* has accepted the *Contractor*'s design of the *works*, there is no restraint on the *Contractor* proceeding even if the design of an item of Equipment has not been accepted.

The *Contractor* can proceed even though he has not obtained acceptance of his Equipment design, including temporary works. The *Project Manager* should seek details of temporary works well in advance of when the work is going to be done (prompted by what he sees on the *Contractor's* programme) so that he can register any dissatisfaction with the proposals in good time. However, responsibility for producing temporary works and Equipment generally which permits the *works* themselves to be completed properly lies with the *Contractor*.

People 24

24.1 This clause gives reasons for not accepting a proposed replacement for a key person. It does not preclude the *Project Manager* accepting a person with qualifications or expertise which are inferior to the listed person, if he is satisfied that such a person will be suitable for the position.

24.2 This clause provides the authority for the *Project Manager*, on behalf of the *Employer*, to have a *Contractor's* employee removed from work on the contract. Possible reasons for asserting this authority include:

- security,
- health and safety (communicable diseases),
- disorderly behaviour prejudicing the *Employer's* operations.

but the *Project Manager* may do it for any reason provided he states what it is.

Co-operation 25

25.1 On many projects there are several contractors and other organisations. These may include public utilities who are to divert their services or provide new services and plant. Somctimes a public utility employs its own contractor but the utility supervises the work. The duty of the *Contractor* to co-operate with Others has been expressed in general terms only, as the detailed requirements will depend on the particular project and Site.

The interface between the contractors and other bodies is often complex. It is important that this work is planned and programmed as far as possible before the start of the contract. The start dates for work should be agreed together with details of the work, its likely duration and facilities required to be provided by and for the *Contractor*. Details of the obligations of the parties at each interface and the timing and programming arrangements should be agreed. This information may conveniently be provided in the form of interface schedules in the Works Information, to ensure that arrangements in the different contracts are 'back-to-back'. It should also be stated which party is to supply and maintain access (e.g. scaffolding, lifting equipment for plant), resources (for testing, etc.) and other services (such as power supply and water supply).

If precise dates are not available, approximate dates should be given in the Works Information. The *Contractor* should then be required to meet the other parties soon after the *starting date*, agree detailed programmes with them and incorporate the information in his own programme.

The *Contractor* is not responsible for the failure of other parties to carry out their work in accordance with the Works Information unless the failure is caused by the *Contractor* not co-operating. The exchange of information on health and safety matters is particularly important in order to comply with the law as well as with the contract.

Subcontracting 26

26.2 This clause provides that the *Contractor* may subcontract parts of the *works*, provided the *Project Manager* accepts the proposed Subcontractors. In the case of proposals for subcontracts for small amounts of technically simple work, acceptance by the *Project Manager* may be a formality.

No provision is included in ECC for nomination of Subcontractors. This is because of the legal and practical problems of accountability which frequently ensue. The principle of the ECC is that the *Contractor* is fully responsible for every aspect of managing the work he has contracted for. Nominating Subcontractors conflicts with this principle and causes many practical problems. Alternatives to nominating Subcontractors whilst achieving similar objectives are:

(a) making the *Contractor* responsible for all work. He may then subcontract parts and the *Project Manager* retains some control over the identity of the Subcontractors provided any withholding of acceptance is for the reason stated.

(b) providing for separate contracts with the *Project Manager* managing the time and physical interfaces between them.

(c) including lists of acceptable Subcontractors for particular tasks in the Works Information.

Where national or international law requires, the Works Information should include a statement of award criteria for subcontracts.

Acceptance of a Subcontractor cannot be withdrawn later, providing his appointment complies with these clauses.

26.3 The NEC Engineering and Construction Subcontract (or the NEC Professional Services Contract for design work) is expected to be used as recommended in the Latham Report (July 1994). However, in the case of many small and straightforward subcontracts, overseas contracts or where the requirements of a particular industry make the ECS or the PSC inappropriate, the *Project Manager* may agree to other subcontract conditions being used.

Approval from Others 27

27.1 This clause requires the *Contractor* to obtain the requisite approvals for his design from planning authorities, nuclear inspectorates and others who may have the duty or authority to approve his design. The contract is silent about the *Contractor* obtaining approval from outside bodies to other aspects of his work such as road closures or access for major items of Equipment.

Access to the work 28

28.1 It is important that the *Project Manager* and *Supervisor* have the right to visit places where work is being carried out. This includes right of access to suppliers' and Subcontractors' premises to permit them to inspect and test work as necessary and to check progress.

Instructions 29

29.1 Various clauses in the contract give the *Project Manager* and the *Supervisor* authority to issue instructions to the *Contractor*. It is important that these instructions are given within the limits and for the reasons expressly stated. If, for any reason, the *Contractor* disagrees with an instruction, his remedy is to follow the disputes procedure described in Section 9, not to refuse to obey the instruction.

MAIN OPTION CLAUSES

Option F: Management contract

Providing the Works 20

20.2 In a management contract, the core clauses and this clause state how the *Contractor* is to Provide the Works by identifying what he is to do himself and what he is to subcontract.

The effects are shown in the table below. This also shows how the *Contractor* is paid by relating the different categories of work to the Actual Cost and the Fee.

Providing the Works			
Contractor does not subcontract	*Contractor* may subcontract	*Contractor* must subcontract	
Management of – the *Contractor*'s design – construction and installation	Other work (not management, construction or installation)which the Works Information does not require to be subcontracted.	Other work (not management, construction or installation) which the Works Information requires to be subcontracted	Construction and installation
Covered by the Fee		Included in Actual Cost	

3 Time

CORE CLAUSES

Starting and Completion **30**

The period of time within which the *Contractor* is required to Provide the Works is not stated. Instead, the *starting date* and the *completion date* are given in the Contract Data. This enables tenderers to know when the work may begin. Both *starting date* and *completion date* may be adjusted by agreement before the Contract Date.

For many contracts, the contract period is decided by the *Employer* enabling the *completion date* to be inserted in the Contract Data before inviting tenders.

Alternatively, the *completion date* may be decided by the tenderers and submitted as part of their offers. If this is done, *Employers* should make clear how tenders are to be assessed, indicating the value to be placed on an early *completion date*.

Sometimes, the *completion date* is decided by the *Employer* but alternative tenders are also invited on the basis of an earlier tendered *completion date*. Again in such a case, the basis of assessing tenders should be made clear to the tenderers.

It is essential for *completion dates* to be stated (by one of the above methods) in a construction contract. Even if the extent of the work is uncertain, which may be the case in a cost reimbursable contract, a time should be stated based on a stated assumed amount of work. If this is not done, extension of time and delay damages provisions cannot be applied.

30.1 The *starting date* in the Contract Data is the date when the *Contractor* can start work. He cannot start work on Site until the first *possession date*. The *possession dates* are stated in the Contract Data. In contracts for the manufacture and installation of plant, or when the *Contractor* has to do significant pre-planning or design, the *possession dates* may be some time after the *starting date*.

30.2 The *Project Manager* is responsible for certifying Completion, as defined in Clause 11.2(13), within one week of Completion. Normally, the *Contractor* will ask for the certificate as soon as he considers he is entitled to it, but such a request is not essential.

The programme **31**

31.1 Provision has been made for a programme either to be identified in the Contract Data part two at the Contract Date or to be submitted by the *Contractor* within a period stated in the Contract Data part one.

The programme is an important document for administering the contract. It enables the *Project Manager* and *Contractor* to monitor progress and to assess the time effects of compensation events including changes to the Completion Date.

Employers may wish to have programmes submitted with tenders in order to judge whether a tenderer has fully understood his obligations and whether he is likely to be able to carry out the work within the stated time, using the methods and resources proposed. Any doubts on these matters can then be resolved after submission of tenders.

If the *Employer* asks tenderers to submit programmes with their tenders, it is possible that a tenderer may show his planned Completion before the Completion Date stated in the Contract Data. In such a case the *Employer* may wish to negotiate a revision to the Completion Date stated in the Contract Data so that it becomes the same as the date of planned Completion indicated in the programme. If the Completion Date in the Contract Data is not changed, the terminal float remains and the provisions of Clause 63.3 regarding delays due to compensation events apply.

Acceptance of a programme, unlike acceptance of the *Contractor*'s design, is not a condition precedent to the *Contractor* proceeding with the work. Failure to accept a revised programme does not require the *Contractor* to stop work.

31.2 This clause lists the information which the *Contractor* is required to show on each programme submitted for acceptance. It consists of:

- dates which are stated in the Contract Data or the Works Information
- dates decided by the *Contractor*,
- method statements,
- order and timing,
- float and, separately, time risk allowances,
- health and safety requirements, and
- other information required in the Works Information

Method statements for the *Contractor*'s operations consist of descriptions of the construction methods as well as details of the resources, including Equipment, he intends to use. Thus any reference in the contract to the programme includes these method statements. This means, for example that a *Contractor*'s quotation submitted in relation to a compensation event which includes a revised programme must also include any revised methods of construction and resources. A revised programme would be necessary even if only methods and resources were changed without there being any change to the order or timing of the activities.
Separate references to 'float' and to 'time risk allowances' are included in Clause 31.2. It is important that they are each clearly identifiable on the programme.

The *Contractor*'s time risk allowances are to be shown on his programme as allowances attached to the duration of each activity or to the duration of parts of the *works*. These allowances are owned by the *Contractor* as part of his realistic planning to cover his risks. They should be either clearly identified as such in the programme or included in the time periods allocated to specific activities. It follows that they should be retained in the assessment of any delay to planned Completion due to the effect of a compensation event.

Float is any spare time within the programme after the time risk allowances have been included. It is normally available to accommodate the time effects of a compensation event in order to mitigate or avoid any delay to planned Completion. However, in accordance with Clause 63.3, float attached to the whole programme (ie any float between planned Completion and the Completion Date) is not available. Any delay to planned Completion due to a compensation event therefore results in the same delay to the Completion Date. (See further notes on Clause 63.3.)

It is important that the time risk allowances included by the *Contractor* in a programme submitted for acceptance are realistic. If they are not, the *Project Manager* may refer to the third bullet of Clause 31.3 and refuse acceptance.

The provision for health and safety matters should allow for any statutory procedures, as well as those specifically mentioned in the Works Information.

The programme is also to show dates when the *Contractor* requires information, facilities, possession, etc which are to be provided to him by the *Employer*. Where there is a large amount of *Contractor* design, it may be appropriate for the Works Information to ask for an increasing amount of detail to be shown on the programme as the design is developed.

31.3 This clause lists reasons why a *Project Manager* may decide not to accept a programme or a revised programme. Any failure by the *Project Manager* to accept a programme for reasons other than those noted is a compensation event (Clause 60.1(4)). The *Project Manager* is required to respond within two weeks but if the reply is non-acceptance, the *Contractor* is required to re-submit, within the *period for reply*.

Revising the programme 32

32.1 This clause lists the matters which are to be shown on a revised programme. It should record the actual progress achieved on each operation and the reprogramming of future operations. It should also show the effects of implemented compensation events and early warning matters. If a compensation event affects the timing of future operations, a revised programme indicating the effects is to be submitted as part of the *Contractor*'s quotation (Clause 62.2). The revised programme should also show proposals for dealing with delays, Defects and any changes the *Contractor* wishes to make.

Failure by the *Contractor* to submit revised programmes, is of considerable disadvantage to the *Contractor* in that if a compensation event occurs, the *Project Manager* may assess it entirely on the basis of his own judgement. Thus it is in the *Contractor*'s interests to keep the programme up to date.

32.2 The *Project Manager* should note, in reviewing a submitted revised programme, any changes to the dates by which the *Employer* is required to provide information, facilities, possession, etc. He should be prepared to accept a programme with earlier dates if this is acceptable to the *Employer*. After acceptance, any subsequent failure by the *Employer* to meet these earlier dates is a compensation event.

Possession of the Site 33

33.1 The dates on which the *Contractor* may enter and take possession of the various parts of the Site are stated in the Contract Data. In many cases it may be possible to give possession of the whole Site on the *starting date*. In other cases, particularly where there are several contractors on the Site, this may not be possible. The *Contractor* must then programme his activities according to the dates when he can gain possession.

The *Contractor* may not require possession on the dates stated in the Contract Data, in which case he should show on his programme the later dates. These then supersede those in the Contract Data and become obligatory on the *Employer*.

33.2 'Possession' does not mean exclusive possession since there may be other contractors who need to be present on parts of the Site to carry out their work. 'Possession' means the authority to occupy the Site in order to carry out the obligations which the *Contractor* has under the contract.

Where the Site is occupied by more than one contractor, it is important that the interfaces are defined in the Works Information. Any services to be provided by one contractor to another or by or to the *Employer*, should also be stated. Responsibility for the provision and maintenance of facilities should also be stated. Examples of these facilities are

- access roads,
- scaffolding,
- cranes and hoists,
- welfare,
- security arrangements,
- storage,
- power supplies,
- water,
- compressed air and
- telephone.

In addition, the health and safety requirements with which each contractor is required to comply should be stated in the Works Information. This is particularly important for sites occupied by several contractors. If Option U is used the principle contractor and the planning supervisor should be identified in the Works Information.

Failure by the *Employer* to provide the facilities and services stated in the Works Information is a compensation event under Clause 60.1(3). Failure by the *Contractor* to provide the facilities and services stated in the Works Information results in his having to pay any cost incurred by the *Employer*.

The *Contractor* retains possession of the Site until take-over. After that time, the *Employer* is required to allow access to enable the *Contractor* to finish any outstanding work and to repair Defects (Clause 43.3).

'Providing facilities and services' is not to be confused with the *Employer*'s use of the *works*. The Works Information should include details of the facilities and services which the *Employer* requires during the construction operations. This particularly applies where the *Contractor* is required to work in an area where the *Employer* needs to continue working, or when he requires an existing facility to be maintained. For example, in road construction projects, traffic must continue to flow either on temporary diversions or on the partially constructed *works*. Details of the programming and how the *Contractor* provides for this traffic is usually left to the *Contractor*. In complex traffic management schemes, it may be necessary for the *Employer* to prepare full details in advance, and include these in the Works Information.

Instructions to stop or not to start work 34

34.1 This clause gives the *Project Manager* authority to control the stopping and restarting of work for any reason, for example, where there is risk of injury to people or damage to property. An instruction given constitutes a compensation event but, if it arises from a fault of the *Contractor*, the *Contractor* must bear the cost (Clause 61.1). In certain circumstances, if the *Project Manager* fails to instruct the restart of work within 13 weeks of instructing work to stop, either Party may be entitled to terminate the contract under Clause 95.6.

Taking over 35

35.1 If the *Employer* starts to use part of the *works*, take-over of that part occurs at that time (Clause 35.3). If Option L is included in the contract, and the *works* are divided into *sections*, Completion of a *section* results in the *Employer* having to take over the *section* within two weeks of its Completion (Clause 35.2).

If the *Employer* and the *Contractor* agree that part of the *works* or of a *section* should be taken over early, whether or not the Employer starts to use it, before the rest of the *works* or of a *section*, they may of course do so. This amounts to a change to the contract. As part of the terms of such an agreement, any delay damages should be reduced to represent the proportion of the cost of delay which is obviated by the release of that part of the *works*. The reduction of delay damages pro rata according to the value of the part taken over, is too arbitrary to represent a genuine estimate of the reduced damages which might be suffered by the *Employer*. Reduced damages should be separately calculated on a similar basis to the damages stated in the contract, and included in the agreement.

35.2 The *Employer* may have good reasons for not wishing to take over the *works* before the Completion Date. If so, this should be stated in the Contract Data. For example, the work in this contract may be part of a larger scheme such that there is no advantage to the *Employer* in its early completion. If the Contract Data is silent on this, the *Employer* is required to take over the *works* within two weeks of Completion.

35.3 If the *Employer* uses part of the *works* before Completion has been certified, he is deemed to have taken over on the date that he uses it, and a compensation event occurs unless the takeover is for a reason stated in the Works Infomation or to suit the *Contractor*'s method of working. (See notes on Clause 60.1(15).) The *Employer* is then responsible for providing access so that the *Contractor* can correct Defects which will include completing outstanding work (Clause 43.3).

Acceleration 36 Acceleration means bringing the Completion Date forward. This differs from usage in many contracts where 'acceleration' means speeding up the work to ensure that the Completion Date is achieved. If the *Project Manager* is concerned that delay which has already occurred may result in the Completion Date not being achieved, he can instruct the *Contractor* to produce a revised programme under Clause 32.2 showing how he intends to recover the time he has lost.

36.1
36.2 These clauses allow the *Project Manager* to obtain a quotation for acceleration from the *Contractor*. There is no remedy if it is not produced, or if the *Contractor*'s quotation is unacceptable. Acceleration can only be by agreement between the *Project Manager* and the *Contractor*. It cannot be imposed on the *Contractor* without his agreement.

An *Employer* who foresees the possibility of requiring acceleration should consider using Options C, D or E when deciding contract strategy, since acceleration agreements are more likely to be achieved under these options than under Option A or B.

MAIN OPTION CLAUSES

Option A and C

The programme 31

31.4 The activities on the *activity schedule* and those on the programme should be compatible in order to make assessment of compensation events and financial forecasting easier. However, the programme may contain more activities than the *activity schedule*.

Options C, D, E and F

Acceleration 36

36.5 The Engineering and Construction Subcontract contains a similar acceleration clause. If the *Contractor* and a Subcontractor agree in principle to propose an acceleration to the subcontract work, the proposal should be submitted by the *Contractor* to the *Project Manager* for acceptance. If the *Project Manager* agrees with the proposal in principle, he may instruct the *Contractor* to submit a quotation under Clause 36.1. The *Project Manager* has no obligation to accept the quotation and there is no remedy if he does not (see Clause 60.1(9)).

The *Project Manager* can in this way exercise control of the financial consequences for the *Employer*. This clause prevents the *Contractor* choosing to accelerate a subcontract for reasons beneficial to himself but detrimental to the *Employer*.

Options A and B

There is no equivalent to Clause 36.5 in Options A and B. This is because there are no direct financial consequences to the *Employer* resulting from an acceleration of a subcontract which arises from an agreement solely between the *Contractor* and a Subcontractor.

4 Testing and Defects

CORE CLAUSES

The *Contractor*'s responsibility for quality is part of his duty to Provide the Works (Clause 20.1) as defined in Clause 11.2(4).

The quality standards to be achieved by the *Contractor* should be specified in the Works Information in part one of the Contract Data. These standards provide the basis on which the existence of a Defect is judged (Clause 11.2(15)). The *Supervisor* acts on the *Employer*'s behalf to check the *Contractor*'s attainment of the specified standards.

Quality systems

If quality systems are required in a project, they should be initiated by the *Employer* at an early stage, such as at the early design stages.

Requirements in the ECC for quality systems, can be accommodated in two ways as follows.

(a) The *Employer* specifies requirements for quality management procedures in the Works Information in part one of the Contract Data.

(b) The *Employer* requires the *Contractor* to provide details of his quality plan in the Works Information.

Tests and inspections 40

40.1 Clause 40 does not apply to tests and inspections done by the *Contractor* at his own discretion and for his own purposes.

40.2 Tests should be specified in the Works Information with respect to

- the nature of the tests,
- when they are to be done,
- where they are to be done,
- who does the test,
- who provides materials, facilities and samples, and
- their objectives and procedures.

Additional tests may be instructed by the *Project Manager* by changing the Works Information. This is a compensation event under Clause 60.1(1) unless the test is either required to check for a Defect and one is found (Clause 60.1(10)) or it is a repeat test. Such instructions should specify details of the test.

When tests are to be done

The timing of tests should be stated in the Works Information as should whether payment or authorisation to proceed to the next stage of the work depends on the test results.

Key times include the following.

- Before payment for or marking of Equipment or Plant and Materials (Clause 71.1).
- Before delivery to the Working Areas (Clause 41.1).
- Before Completion. The Works Information should state which tests have to be passed before Completion.
- After take-over but before the *defects date*. Tests required during this period will usually be part of the *Employer*'s commissioning. In the case of process plants, they may involve production materials which the *Employer* may need to have under his direct control. Such tests may be carried out by the *Supervisor* on the *Employer*'s behalf or by the *Contractor*. It is possible that the completed parts of the *works* may be put into operation by the *Employer* before completing his own tests. A 'sunset' Clause (40.5) is

included to avoid the possibility of payments conditional on the successful completion of a *Supervisor*'s test being withheld if the test has not been carried out by the *defects date*. This provision does not apply to tests which have to be repeated due to discovery of a Defect.

Failure by the *Supervisor* to carry out his tests promptly is a compensation event (Clause 60.1(11)) if it causes unnecessary delay to the *Contractor*.

Where tests are to be done

The Works Information should state the location of each test if it is not to be carried out within the Working Areas. Items which may come into this category include heavy structural units, mechanical and electrical plant, computer and other proprietary equipment.

Who does the test

The Works Information should specify who is responsible for carrying out each test or for arranging for it to be carried out. The choice will be between the following.

- The *Contractor*, including his Subcontractors and suppliers.Where the *Contractor* is to arrange for a test to be carried out by an independent or public authority, the Works Information should include the name of the authority, the tests and the form in which the results are to be supplied.
- The *Supervisor*.

Who provides materials, facilities and samples

The Works Information should state who provides the materials and apparatus necessary for each test. The required items may include the following.

- Samples of materials to be tested. These are normally provided by the *Contractor*, his Subcontractors or suppliers.
- Testing apparatus, test loads, measuring instruments. These could be provided by the *Employer*, the *Supervisor* or the *Contractor* (including his Subcontractors or suppliers) or hired from an independent or public authority.
- Testing facilities such as a Site laboratory (normally provided by the *Contractor* but sometimes by the *Employer*) or laboratories off-Site (normally those of an independent company or authority).
- Services for the tests (water, electricity, air, steam, etc.) which are
    - off-Site — normally provided by the testing authority being used,
    - on-Site, before take-over — normally provided by the *Contractor* from the services available on Site but sometimes augmented by the *Employer* when special services are required or
    - on-Site, after take-over — normally provided by the *Employer*.
- Materials for use in the tests (including performance tests) — normally provided by the *Employer* or by a specialist Subcontractor or supplier.
- Fuel for the tests (gas, coal, oil etc) — normally provided by the *Employer*
- Provision and disposal of production materials — normally provided or disposed of by the *Employer*.

Objectives, procedures, etc.

The objectives, procedures and the standards to be satisfied should be specified in the Works Information. Types of tests may include the following.

- Checking setting out, line, level, verticality.
- Measuring movements, settlement and soil characteristics in earthworks.
- Testing the properties of materials to be incorporated in the *works* for strength, durability, appearance, brittleness, flexibility, corrosion resistance, etc.
- Testing the structural, mechanical or pressure resisting strength of Plant, piping systems, structures or other parts of the *works*.

- Testing the performance, accuracy and reliability of control systems and associated instruments and servo-mechanisms incorporated in the *works*.
- Testing the reliability, safety and effectiveness of electrical, mechanical and other systems incorporated in the *works*.
- Testing the performance of the *works* including the performance of items of Plant to prove that they perform as specified in the Works Information.

40.3 This clause deals with four matters.

- the procedure for notifying when testing is to be done,
- the requirement to notify test results,
- the timing of notifying the *Supervisor* of testing or inspection, and
- the right of the *Supervisor* to observe the *Contractor*'s tests.

The *Contractor* and *Supervisor* are each required to give the other advance notice of tests which each is to carry out. This enables both parties to be fully informed and to take any action they wish to take. If, for example, testing reveals that some work does not comply with the Works Information, early discussion of the consequences is likely to be required. Notification of tests and their results is required before further testing or inspection is rendered impossible or impracticable. For example, the results of a drain test should be notified before the drain is covered up, or the result of a test of reinforcing steel should be notified before concrete is placed around the reinforcement. Failure by the *Contractor* to notify the *Supervisor* of a test or inspection may deprive the *Contractor* of compensation for a search, even if no Defect is found (Clause 60.1(10)).

40.4 A Defect is defined in Clause 11.2(15). Any repeat test or inspection of work after a Defect has been corrected is not a compensation event.

A Defect may make it impossible to reconstruct the work affected in accordance with the Works Information. For example, piles which have been installed outside the specified tolerances may have disturbed the original ground such that the construction of the foundation as shown on the drawings has become impossible. The early warning procedure (Clause 16) requires early discussion of the matter. Possible solutions include changing the Works Information after redesign or accepting the Defect (Clause 44).

40.5 Under this clause, the *Supervisor* is required to carry out testing and inspection for which he is responsible so that unnecessary delay to the work is avoided. If unnecessary delay occurs a compensation event results (Clause 60.1(11)). Some payments to the *Contractor* may be conditional upon doing particular tests to show that the work has been carried out satisfactorily. If the *Supervisor* causes unnecessary delay, such payments may become due after the *defects date* whether or not the tests are carried out.

Testing and inspection before delivery 41

41.1 The purpose of this clause is to avoid expense in having to transport Plant and Materials back to the place of manufacture if testing and inspection reveal Defects.

Searching and notifying Defects 42

42.1 A Defect as defined in Clause 11.2(15) is one for which the *Contractor* is responsible. A fault in a design provided by the *Employer* is not a Defect. If a defect in the *works* is suspected, the *Supervisor* may instruct the *Contractor* to search in order to determine responsibility for the defect.

If a search is instructed and a defect is found which is due to a fault in the *Employer*'s design (i.e. no Defect as defined is found), the instruction to search is a compensation event (Clause 60.1(10)) and responsibility for further action belongs to the *Project Manager*. He may decide to change the design and instruct the *Contractor* accordingly. This would constitute a change to the Works Information which would be a further compensation event (Clause 60.1(1)).

If the defect is due to non-compliance with the Works Information, it is a Defect and does not result in a compensation event. It is then the *Contractor*'s responsibility to correct the Defect so that the work complies with the Works Information.

The clause also includes extra tests and inspections not specified in the Works Information within the meaning of 'searching'. Whether or not such tests are compensation events is determined using Clause 60.1(10).

42.2 The intention of this clause is to enable Defects to be identified as soon as possible so that they can be dealt with promptly.

Correcting Defects 43

43.1 The periods for the notification and correction of Defects are illustrated in Figure 3.

The *defects date* is defined in the Contract Data as a date which is a stated period of time after Completion. Normal practice for most civil engineering and construction contracts in the UK would be a period of 12 months. For process plant, longer periods, commonly 3 years but up to 7 or even 10 years in special circumstances, may be appropriate.

Defects may be notified for correction by the *Contractor* at any time before the *defects date*.

The *Supervisor*, *Project Manager* or *Employer* may inform the *Contractor* of Defects after the *defects date* but the *Contractor*'s responsibility for them will be limited according to the law governing the contract.

The *Contractor* is responsible for correcting Defects, whether or not they have been notified. If a Defect affects the work stated in the Works Information as to be done before Completion (Clause 11.2(13)), it will have to be corrected to avoid delaying Completion. The Works Information may include a requirement for satisfactory completion of certain tests and acceptance by the *Project Manager* of standards which will enable the *Employer* to use the *works*.

This clause also provides that the *Contractor* has to correct notified Defects which do not delay Completion before the end of the *defect correction period.*

The *defect correction period* (DCP) stated in part one of the Contract Data only affects the timing of correcting Defects after Completion. Before Completion the *Contractor* decides how quickly he should correct Defects to avoid delaying Completion. The length of the *defect correction period* to be given in the Contract Data depends on

- the kind of Defects likely to be outstanding after Completion and the time needed for their correction,
- the urgency of the *Employer*'s need for their correction and
- the ease with which access can be given to correct them.

43.2 At the *defects date*, or the end of the last *defect correction period* if later, the *Supervisor* issues a Defects Certificate. This will be used by the *Project Manager* in assessing the final amount due to the *Contractor* (Clause 50.1). The certificate is defined in Clause 11.2(16)).

43.3 The procedure in this Clause allows the *Contractor* access to complete outstanding work and correct other Defects after the *Employer* has taken over. Normally, this work can only be done at the *Employer*'s convenience as, after Completion, the *Employer* is obliged to take over the *works*. The clause also includes a procedure for extending the *defect correction period* if necessary.

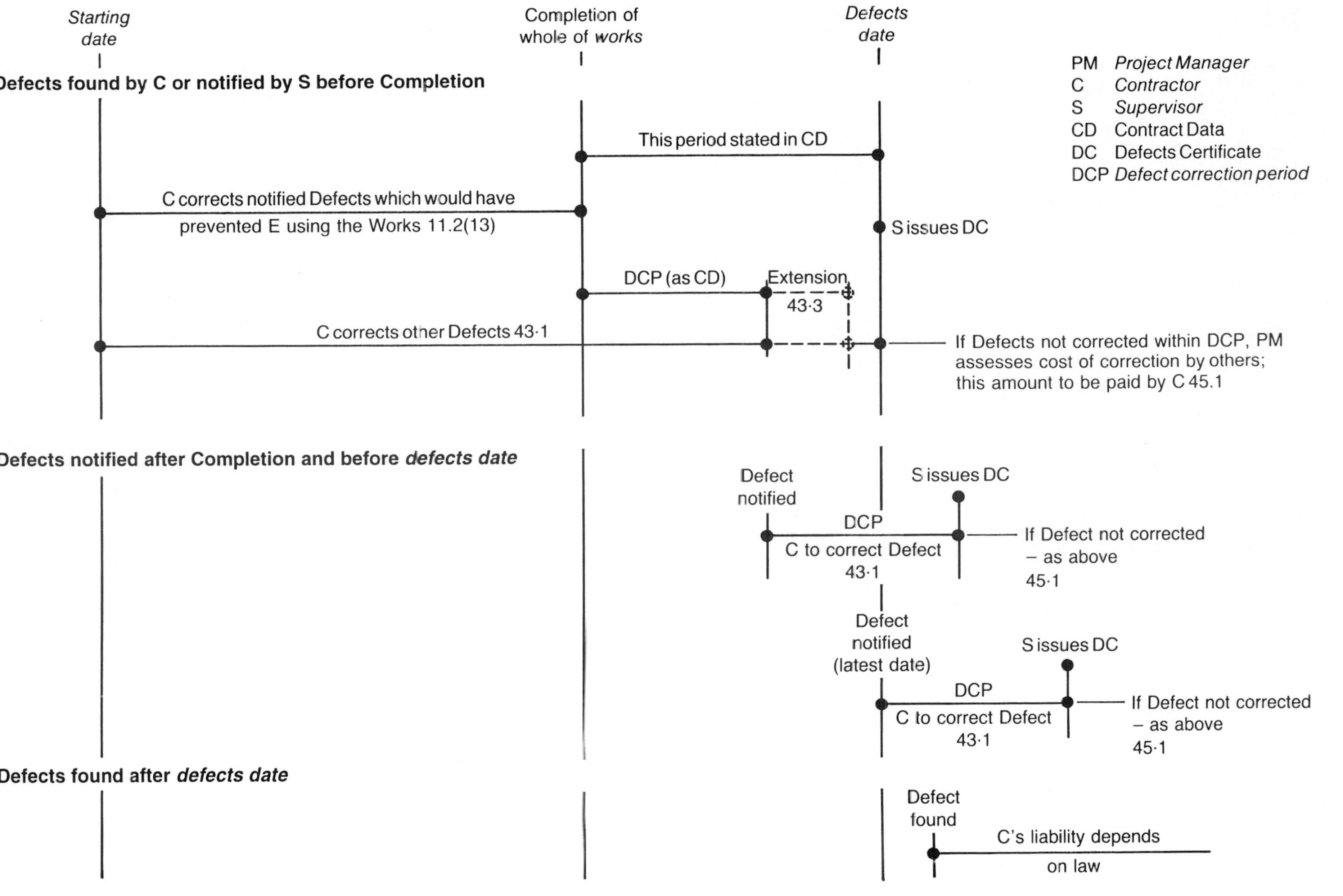

Figure 3. Notification and correction of Defects

Accepting Defects 44

44.1 Although a Defect may be minor, its correction may be costly to the *Contractor* and may delay Completion by a considerable time. Its correction may also cause inconvenience to the *Employer* out of all proportion to the benefits gained. This clause gives a procedure within the contract for accepting a Defect in these circumstances. Either the *Contractor* or the *Project Manager* may propose a change to the Works Information solely to avoid correction of a Defect. The other is not obliged to accept the proposal.

44.2 The *Contractor*'s quotation for the proposed change will show a reduction in either time or price or both. In some cases the reduction may be nominal. For example, a nominal price reduction may be acceptable if the effect of the change to the Works Information is not detrimental and if the alternative of correcting the Defect will reduce the likelihood of prompt Completion.

If the quotation is not acceptable, no further action is necessary. If the quotation is accepted by the *Project Manager*, its implementation follows the compensation event procedure.

Uncorrected Defects 45

45.1 The assessment of the cost of having a Defect corrected by other people does not trigger an assessment under Clause 50.1. This means that most of such amounts accumulate until the *defects date* unless there has been Completion of a *section* of the *works* and, a *defect correction period* ends before Completion of the whole of the *works*. When the *Project Manager* is carrying out the assessment following the issue of the Defects Certificate, he will offset the cost of these uncorrected Defects against the release of the second half of the retention money if Option P is included. This emphasises the need to make the retention sufficient to cover the likely cost of uncorrected Defects at the *defects date*. This is one of the reasons for the retention arrangement. Quite a high percentage retention should be set in these circumstances because its main purpose is to cover the cost of dealing with uncorrected Defects after Completion. The retention free amount should be set as a significant proportion of the contract price so that the retention does not start to accumulate until towards the end of the contract period. It should then produce a significant fund which remains in the *Employer*'s hands until the *defects date* when the extent of the cost of uncorrected Defects is known.

5 Payment

Payment mechanisms for the main options

The different payment mechanisms for the six main options are based on the use of two key terms:

- The Prices and
- The Price for Work Done to Date (PWDD)

Each term is defined for each main option in Clause 11.2 as set out in the following table. Abbreviations used in the table are

AS *activity schedule*
BQ *bill of quantities*
AC Actual Cost

Option	The Prices	The Price for Work Done to Date (PWDD)
A	AS prices for activities 11.2(20)	Total of the Prices for completed activities 11.2(24)
B	BQ rates and prices 11.2(21)	Quantities of completed work at BQ rates and proportions of lump sums prices 11.2(25)
C	AS prices for activities 11.2(20)	AC paid + Fee 11.2(23)
D	BQ rates and prices 11.2(21)	AC paid + Fee 11.2(23)
E	AC + Fee 11.2(19)	AC paid + Fee 11.2(23)
F	AC + Fee 11.2(19)	AC accepted for payment + Fee 11.2(22)

Actual Cost is also defined for each main option in Clause 11.2.

These terms defined in the main option clauses, when used in conjunction with the core clauses in Section 5, establish the payment mechanism for each main option.

The Price for Work Done to Date (PWDD) is the main component of the amount due to the *Contractor* (see notes on Clause 50). The use made of the Prices varies between the main options.

Identified and defined terms **11**

Option A

11.2 (24) The PWDD is the *activity schedule* prices for those activities or groups of activities which have been completed according to the criteria stated in Clause 11.2(24).

(20) The Prices are the basis of the PWDD. In the final assessment the PWDD is the total of the Prices of the completed work.It is important that the *Contractor*, when compiling the *activity schedule*, defines activities and groups of activities, completion of which can be recognised without controversy (see earlier notes on 'Preparing the tender documents').

The effect of a compensation event may be to extend the duration of an activity (or group of activities) such that its completion is delayed. The delay may result in a delay to payment if the activity completion occurs after the assessment date by which the activity was originally expected to have been completed.

A compensation event which causes a delay to payment for an activity is assessed using the Schedule of Cost Components which permits financing charges for such a delay to be included in the assessment of the compensation event. In exceptional circumstances, where the delay would otherwise cause a seriously adverse effect on the *Contractor*'s cash flow, the *Project Manager* may agree to splitting the activity into two so that payment can be made for the completed work. In deciding whether to agree to this, the *Project Manager* should take account of the extent to which the *Contractor* is collaborating through the early warning procedure and by keeping the Accepted Programme up to date. He should also take account of any delays to the activity or overall programme which are the fault of the *Contractor*.

(28) The only use of Actual Cost in Option A is as the basis of the assessment of compensation events. Actual Cost is the cost of the components listed in the Schedule of Cost Components (see later notes) for work done by the *Contractor* and Subcontractors. The cost of preparing quotations for compensation events is specifically excluded (see notes on Clause 62.1).

Option B

11.2 (25) The PWDD is calculated using the *bill of quantities* rates and lump sums and the total quantity of work completed according to the definition and criteria stated in this clause.

(21) The Prices are the basis of the PWDD. In the final account, the PWDD is the total of the Prices of the final quantity of work completed. In this way, the *Contractor* is paid for the actual quantities of work done, not those in the original *bill of quantities*. Option B is therefore a remeasurement contract. It can be used for building contracts where remeasurement is not traditional.

(28) The only use of Actual Cost in Option B is as the basis of the assessment of compensation events. Actual Cost is the cost of the components listed in the Schedule of Cost Components (see later notes) for work done by the *Contractor* and Subcontractors. The cost of preparing quotations for compensation events is specifically excluded (see notes on Clause 62.1).

Options C and D

11.2 (23) The PWDD is Actual Cost paid plus the Fee as in the cost reimbursable Option E. Costs committed by the *Contractor*, but not yet paid, and invoices received, but not paid, are excluded.

(20) (21) The Prices (using an *activity schedule* for Option C and a *bill of quantities* for Option D) are not used to determine the PWDD but are used as the target in determining (at Completion and in the final assessment) the *Contractor*'s share (see notes on Clause 53).

(27) Actual Cost is calculated from the components listed in the Schedule of Cost Components (see later notes) for work done by the *Contractor* together with payments due to Subcontractors. Actual Cost is used in calculating the PWDD and in assessing compensation events. Actual Cost excludes Disallowed Cost as defined separately in Clause 11.2(30). The cost of preparing quotations for compensation events is included in Actual Cost.

Option E

11.2 (23) The PWDD is Actual Cost plus the Fee. Costs committed by the *Contractor* but not yet paid, and invoices received, but not paid, are excluded.

(19) The PWDD becomes the total of the Prices in the final assessment.

(27) Actual Cost is calculated from the components listed in the Schedule of Cost Components (see later notes) for work done by the *Contractor* together with payments due to Subcontractors. Actual Cost is used in calculating the PWDD and in assessing compensation events. Actual Cost excludes Disallowed Cost as defined separately in Clause 11.2(30). The cost of preparing quotations for compensation events is included in Actual Cost.

Option F

11.2 (22) The PWDD is Actual Cost accepted for payment (not necessarily paid) plus the Fee. The *Contractor* is due a payment from the *Employer* when he has accepted a payment to a Subcontractor but not necessarily paid it.

(19) The PWDD becomes the total of the Prices in the final assessment.

(26) Actual Cost comprises solely the payments due to Subcontractors. It is used to calculate the PWDD and in assessing compensation events. It excludes Disallowed Cost as defined separately in Clause 11.2(29). (See also notes on Option F under 'Contract Strategy'.)

CORE CLAUSES

Assessing the amount due 50

50.1 This clause defines 'assessment dates' from which the dates of both certification and payment are calculated. The first assessment date is determined by the *Project Manager*, preferably after discussion with the *Contractor*, with a view to satisfying the internal procedures of both the *Employer* and the *Contractor*. Thereafter, assessment dates occur after each *assessment interval* until Completion of the whole of the *works*, when a further assessment date occurs.

After Completion, assessments are not made at regular intervals but there are two situations which create assessment dates.

- When a certified payment of a change in the amount due is found to be incorrect. The correcting payment is then assessed.
- When a payment is made late. Assessment of the interest on the late payment is then made.

Either of these situations could occur following a decision of the *Adjudicator* or the *tribunal* and a final assessment date would follow the decision.

The final assessment date will be either

- four weeks after the date when the *Supervisor* issues the Defects Certificate (the period of four weeks allows time for the *Project Manager* to assess the cost of correcting Defects listed on the Defects Certificate (Clause 45.1)) or
- after the final decision of the *Adjudicator* or the *tribunal*.

50.2 The core of the amount due to the *Contractor* is the Price for Work Done to Date (PWDD). All other payments except advanced payments (e.g. for Plant and Materials outside the Working Areas, retention, repayments of advanced payment, damages, VAT and sales tax) are added to or deducted from the PWDD to calculate the amount due. The content of PWDD varies according to which main option is used (see earlier notes on payment mechanisms).

Under the UK VAT regulations, payment of VAT by the *Employer* to the *Contractor* is made in response to a VAT invoice provided by the *Contractor*. The *Project Manager* and the *Contractor* should therefore make arrangements to ensure that:

- the correct levels of VAT are included in the amount due and
- the *Contractor*'s VAT invoice is provided for attachment to the *Project Manager*'s certificate.

If the *Employer* uses a self billing system, a *Contractor*'s invoice is not needed and the *Employer*'s remittance document becomes the VAT invoice.

50.3 This clause is designed to provide a powerful motivation on the *Contractor* to submit a programme which contains the information required by the contract. The clause imposes a test to determine whether a quarter of the Price for Work Done to Date should be retained.

If a programme was required to be submitted with the tender the programme is identified in the Contract Data at the Contract Date. In this situation an Accepted Programme already exists and no amount can be retained.

If a programme is not identified in the Contract Data it is of vital importance to the management of a contract that a programme complying with Clause 31 is submitted within the period stated in the Contract Data. If a programme is not submitted, the retention can be withheld.

The test for withholding this retention is one of submission of a programme by the *Contractor*, not acceptance by the *Project Manager*. This avoids retention being imposed as a result of a delay by the *Project Manager* in deciding whether or not to accept the programme.

Clause 50.3 does not apply to any subsequent revision of an Accepted Programme. A different incentive exists on the *Contractor* to keep the Accepted Programme up-to-date (see the notes on Clause 64.2).

50.4 Although assessments of the amount due are the responsibility of the *Project Manager* (Clause 50.1), he takes account of any submissions by the *Contractor* and provides details of his assessment.

Payment 51

51.1 The latest dates by which the *Project Manager* certifies payments are fixed throughout a contract as each is related to an assessment date. In the majority of cases, certification will be of payment to the *Contractor*.

51.2 The latest dates by which payments are due to be made are also fixed throughout a contract as each is related to an assessment date. Interest is due to the receiving party, either *Employer* or *Contractor*, if a payment is not made within the stated period after the assessment date. The *Project Manager* should

- certify payment as early as possible within the week after the assessment date.
- before the Contract Date, check that the *Employer* is able to pay within the stated period after the assessment date.

The principle that interest is due from the latest date that payment should have been made is applied throughout the contract.

51.3 The same principles on interest due apply to later corrections to certified amounts (including any due to compensation events) made by the *Project Manager* or decided by the *Adjudicator* or the *tribunal*. The last sentence of this clause refers to interest being calculated from the date upon which the increased amount would have been certified if there had been no dispute or mistake.

51.4 Similar principles apply when no certificate is issued as apply when a certificate is issued for an incorrect amount. If late certification (for whatever reason) is followed by late payment, interest will also be due on the late payment under Clause 51.2.

51.5 The *interest rate* stated in part one of the Contract Data should be a reliable annual base rate applicable to the territory in which the work is to be done plus a percentage to represent the current commercial rates. This may be, for example, 2% above the base rate. Simple interest at the *interest rate* applies for periods less than one year.

Actual Cost 52

52.1 The definition of Actual Cost in Clause 11.2 varies according to each main option. The definition for Options A and B (Clause 11.2(28)) depends entirely on the Schedule of Cost Components (see later notes). The definition for options C, D and E (Clause 11.2(27)) excludes Disallowed Cost (defined separately in Clause 11.2(30)). Similarly, the definition for option F (Clause 11.2(26)) excludes Disallowed Cost (Clause 11.2(29)). See also notes on Schedule of Cost Components as regards to other costs 'deemed to be included in the *fee percentage*'.

MAIN OPTION CLAUSES

Option A

The *activity schedule* 54

54.1 This clause emphasises that the activity schedule is only a payment document. It cannot be used to determine what the Contractor is to design or build; only to determine payments to the Contractor for what he designs or builds.

54.2 An activity schedule which contains items that do not represent the Contractor's proposed activities and methods of working will create difficulties in determining payments due. Thus it is important that the activity schedule should relate directly to the programme and always be compatible with it.

54.3 This clause states the criteria by which changes to the activity schedule are to be judged. For instance, any change in Prices should not upset the balance of pricing which existed in the original activity schedule. The total of the Prices must not be changed except as a result of a compensation event or an acceleration. The criteria do not attempt to restrict changes to cash flow resulting from revisions to the activity schedule.

Option B

The *bill of quantities* 55

55.1 This clause emphasises that the bill of quantities is only a payment document. It cannot be used to determine what the Contractor is to design or build; only to determine payments to the *Contractor* for what he designs or builds.

Option C

Assessing the amount due 50

50.6 As the Contractor is paid Actual Cost, he is reimbursed by the *Employer* in the same currency as the payments made by him. Nevertheless, the Fee and the Contractor's share are paid in the currency of the contract. Calculations are based on the exchange rates identified in the optional statement for options C, D, E or F in part one of the Contract Data.

Actual Cost 52

52.2 This clause lists the accounts and records which the Contractor is required to keep and which are essential for calculating the Actual Cost. If any further records are required, details should be given in the Works Information.

The Contractor's share 53

53.1 Clause 53.1 states how the *Contractor*'s share is calculated.Clause 53.2 states the
53.2 main principle of target contracts whereby the *Contractor* receives a share of any saving and pays a share of any excess when the final PWDD (Actual Cost plus the Fee) is compared to the target (the total of the Prices).

For example, assume that the Contract Data states that:

- The *Contractor*'s *share percentages* and the *share ranges* are

share range	*Contractor's share percentage*
less than 80%	15%
from 80% to 90%	30%
from 90% to 110%	50%
greater than 110%	20%

If at Completion of the whole of the *works*, the total of the Prices (having been adjusted for compensation events) is £100K, the Contract Data table becomes in effect:

Final PWDD	*Contractor's share percentage*
less than £80K	15%
from £80K to £90K	30%
from £90K to £110K	50%
greater than £110K	20%

Examples

Examples of possible outcomes are:

a) Final PWDD = £75K
Saving under total of the Prices = £25K
Comprising 3 increments

80K	= 5K @15%	=	0.75K
80K to 90K	= 10K @30%	=	3.00K
90K to 110K	= 10K @50%	=	5.00K
Contractor's share (paid by *Employer*)		=	£8.75K

b) Final PWDD = £95K
Saving under total of the Prices = £5K
Comprising 1 increment

90K to 110K	= 5K @50%	=	2.5K
Contractor's share (paid by *Employer*)		=	£2.5K

c) Final PWDD = £115K
Excess over total of the Prices = £15K
Comprising 2 increments

90K to 110K	= 10K @50%	=	5.0K
110K	= 5K @20%	=	1.0K
Contractor's share (paid **to** *Employer*)		=	£6.0K

The other potential source of profit for the *Contractor* is the Fee. The *Contractor*'s *share percentages* should be determined in a particular contract to provide the appropriate level of incentive to the *Contractor* to minimise the final PWDD. The extent of financial risk to the Parties in the event of the final PWDD exceeding the total of the Prices, can be varied between two extremes:

- a guaranteed maximum price to the *Employer* can be achieved by stating the *Contractor*'s *share percentage* to be 100% above that price;
- a minimum Fee to the *Contractor* can be achieved by stating the *Contractor's share* percentage to be 0% above a stated price.

Reference should be made to CIRIA Report 85 for further information and guidance on the working of target contracts.

53.3 Payment of the target share is made in two stages. Firstly, in the payment due
53.4 following Completion of the whole of the *works* and secondly in the final payment made after the issue of the Defects Certificate. In calculating the final *Contractor*'s share, the *Project Manager* should take account of costs incurred which the *Contractor* has not been able to pay (for example because an invoice has not been submitted).

Interim payments of the *Contractor*'s share are not provided for. There are two main reasons for this.

- The Prices tendered by a *Contractor* have the main purpose of establishing the total of the Prices (the target). It is not intended that their build-up should provide a realistic forecast of cash flow and they are unlikely to be comparable with the PWDD at any interim stage.
- Forecasts of both the final PWDD (Actual Cost plus the Fee) and the final total of the Prices would be extremely uncertain at early stages of the contract. Any delays in assessing compensation events would further distort the calculation.

The danger of serious under or over payment of an interim *Contractor*'s share has led to the policy of an estimated payment on Completion which is corrected at assessment of the final amount due.

53.5 This provision is designed to motivate the *Contractor* to investigate and propose changes to the *Employer*'s Works Information which will reduce the Actual Cost. It has the effect of improving the *Contractor*'s share position.

The *activity schedule* **54**

54.1 This clause emphasises the fact that the activity schedule is only a payment document. It cannot be used to determine what the Contractor is to design or build; only to determine the Contractor's share.

54.2 It is important that the activity schedule should relate directly to the programme and always be compatible with it.

54.3 This clause states the criteria by which changes to the activity schedule are to be judged. For instance, any change in Prices should not upset the balance of pricing which existed in the original activity schedule. The total of the Prices must not be changed except as a result of a compensation event or an acceleration.

Option D

Assessing the amount due **50**

50.6 As the Contractor is paid Actual Cost, he is reimbursed by the Employer in the same currency as the payments made by him. Nevertheless, the Fee and Contractor's share are paid in the *currency of the contract*. Calculations are based on the *exchange rates* identified in the optional statement for options C, D E or F in part one of the Contract Data.

Actual Cost 52

52.2 This clause lists the accounts and records which the *Contractor* is required to keep and which are essential for calculating the Actual Cost. If any further records are required, details should be given in the Works Information.

The *Contractor*'s share 53

53.1
53.2 Clause 53.1 states how the *Contractor*'s share is calculated. Clause 53.2 states the main principle of target contracts whereby the *Contractor* receives a share of any saving and pays a share of any excess when the final PWDD (Actual Cost plus the Fee) is compared to the target (the total of the Prices). (See also example and further notes on Clauses 53.1 and 53.2 under option C.)

53.3
53.4 Payment of the target share is made in two stages. Firstly, in the payment due following Completion of the whole of the *works* and secondly in the final payment made after the issue of the Defects Certificate. In calculating the final *Contractor*'s share the *Project Manager* should take account of costs incurred which the *Contractor* has not been able to pay (for example because an invoice has not yet been submitted).

Interim payments of the *Contractor*'s share are not provided for. There are two main reasons for this.

- The Prices tendered by a *Contractor* have the main purpose of establishing the total of the Prices (the target). It is not intended that their build-up should provide a realistic forecast of cash flow and they are unlikely to be comparable with the PWDD at any interim stage.
- Forecasts of both the final PWDD (Actual Cost plus the Fee) and the final total of thc Prices would be extremely uncertain at early stages of the contract. Any delays in assessing compensation events would further distort the calculation.

The danger of serious under or over payment of an interim *Contractor*'s share has led to the policy of an estimated payment on Completion which is corrected at assessment of the final amount due.

53.5 This provision is designed to motivate the *Contractor* to investigate and propose changes to the *Employer*'s Works Information which will reduce the Actual Cost. It has the effect of improving the *Contractor*'s share position.

The *bill of quantities* 55

55.1 This clause emphasises that the *bill of quantities* is only a payment document. It cannot be used to determine what the Contractor is to design or build; only to determine the Contractor's share.

Options E and F

Assessing the amount due 50

50.7 As the Contractor is paid Actual Cost, he is reimbursed by the Employer in the same currency as the payments made by him. Nevertheless, the Fee is paid in the currency of the contract. Calculations are based on the exchange rates identified in the optional statement for options C, D, E or F in part one of the Contract Data.

Actual Cost 52

52.2 This clause lists the accounts and records which the Contractor is required to keep and which are essential for calculating the Actual Cost. If any further records are required, details should be given in the Works Information.

6 Compensation events

CORE CLAUSES

Compensation events 60

Compensation events are events which, if they occur, and do not arise from the Contractor's fault, entitle the *Contractor* to be compensated for any effect the event has on the Prices and the Completion Date. The assessment of a compensation event is always of its effect on both the Prices and the Completion Date. Any event may entitle the *Contractor* to additional payment and also to additional time. In the case of some events, the results may be reduced payment to the *Contractor*. (Further notes on the principles of compensation events are included in the 'Introduction' to these Guidance Notes.)

Compensation events are listed in the core clauses, the options and the Contract Data. The main list is in the core Clause 60.1 which includes compensation events (1) to (18). Events applicable to main options B and D are stated in Clauses 60.4, 60.5, and 60.6. Other compensation events are stated in secondary option Clauses J1.2, T1.1 and U1.1.

Part one of the Contract Data also permits the *Employer* to insert additional compensation events. If he does so, the effect is to take the risk of costs and delay arising from the event from the *Contractor*. The event must be described precisely.

Clause 60.1 does not include an industrial dispute as a compensation event unless it is a dispute classed as an *Employer*'s risk by Clause 80.1. In such a case it becomes a compensation event through Clause 60.1(14). *Employers* vary as to the policy they wish to adopt towards the risk of industrial disputes. Outside the UK the legal, cultural or religious climate can also affect policy.

The following are examples of possible additional compensation events for specific contracts. None are applicable generally.

- The cycle time for tunnel excavation exceeds eight working hours for more than four consecutive cycles for reasons outside the control of the *Contractor*.
- The water level in the estuary at Point A rises to more than 26.00 metres above ordnance datum.
- The minimum wage ordered by the Government of X exceeds $Y per hour.
- The amount of water flowing into the main tunnel exceeds 5000 litres per hour before concreting of the invert is completed.
- Work is stopped to allow a ship to pass on more than 24 occasions in a given period.

Changing the Works Information 60.1 (1)

Variations to the *works* are made by a *Project Manager*'s instruction to change the Works Information. The authority given to the *Project Manager* for this purpose is in Clause 14.3. A variation may comprise deletion or addition of work or alteration to work. It may include changes to the *Employer*'s design, to design criteria or to performance requirements for the *Contractor*'s design. Issue of a revised drawing or specification is a compensation event. Clarifications of previously issued drawings or specifications are only made by changing the Works Information. Consequently all such clarifications are compensation events. There may be many reasons for changing the Works Information. They include changes made in order to eliminate an illegality or impossibility (Clause 19) or to resolve an ambiguity or inconsistency (Clause 17).

The clause states two exceptions to a change to the Works Information being a compensation event.

- The procedure for accepting a Defect is stated in Clause 44. An instruction to change the Works Information after acceptance of the *Contractor*'s quotation under Clause 44.2 is not a compensation event.
- A change to the *Contractor*'s design made at his own request is not a compensation event. The clause also gives precedence to the Works Information in part one of the Contract Data over the Works Information in part two of the Contract Data. Thus the *Contractor* should ensure that the Works Information he prepares and submits with his tender as part two of the Contract Data, complies with the requirements of the Works Information in part one of the Contract Data. (See also notes on Clause 21.2.)

Possession of the Site (2)

The *Employer*'s obligations to give the *Contractor* possession of the Site are stated in Clause 33.1.

Provision by the *Employer* (3)

The Works Information should give details of anything, such as Plant and Materials, which the *Employer* is to provide and of any restrictions on when it is to be provided. The *Contractor* is required to include this information on the programme under Clause 31.2.

Stopping work (4)

Clause 34.1 gives the *Project Manager* the authority to instruct the *Contractor* to stop or not to start work. There are several reasons why the Project Manager may give such an instruction, e.g. for reasons of safety.

Work of the *Employer* or Others (5)

The Works Information should give details of the order and timing of work to be done by the Employer or Others. The Contractor is required to include this information on the programme under Clause 31.2.

Reply to a communication (6)

Various periods are given in particular clauses for reply by the Project Manager and *Supervisor* and a general *period for reply* is given in the Contract Data. The obligation to reply within the relevant period is stated in Clause 13.3.

Objects of value (7)

The procedure for dealing with objects of value or of historical or other interest found within the Site is stated in Clause 73.1.

Changing a decision (8)

The *Project Manager* and *Supervisor* are able to change decisions made under the authority given to them in the contract, in the same way as they made their original decisions.

Witholding or acceptance (9)

Various clauses state reasons why the *Project Manager* is entitled not to accept a submission or proposal from the *Contractor*.

Searching (10)

The *Supervisor* can instruct the *Contractor* to search under Clause 42.1, where the term has a wide meaning. Usually searches are instigated where faulty design, construction or manufacture is suspected.

Delayed tests and inspections (11)

The testing and inspection work to be carried out by the *Supervisor* is stated in the Works Information. Under Clause 40.5, the *Supervisor* is required to do this work without causing unnecessary delay.

Physical conditions 60.1 (12) 60.2 60.3

For many years, it has been the practice in construction contracts for the *Employer* to take the risk of physical conditions which have been described in such terms as 'those which could not reasonably have been foreseen by an experienced contractor'. The interpretation of such clauses has been the source of many disputes,

The criteria which the *Contractor* is assumed to have taken account of in that judgement are given in Clause 60.2. Clause 60.3 states the 'contra proferentem' rule regarding inconsistencies in the Site Information, for which the *Employer* is responsible.

This compensation event is limited to those physical conditions which are encountered within the Site. Since most claims for unforeseen conditions are in respect of ground conditions, the more information concerning ground conditions which is made available to tenderers by the *Employer*, the greater the certainty with which appropriate allowances can be made in tendering. It is important that the ground information provided is both correct and relevant to the risks faced. It may be advisable also to prepare and provide interpretation of factual data, provided this is prepared by a specialist. In this way tenderers are able to tender on a common basis.

One method of reducing disputes on this topic, is to define in the contract the boundary line between the risks carried by the *Employer* and *Contractor*, i.e. to state what tenderers should allow for in their tenders. This can be done, for example, in tunnel works or extensive foundation works by stating the boundary limits. This should be done by using Option Z to state boundary limits covering such matters as:

- soil characteristics,
- levels of rock/soil interface,
- groundwater levels,
- permeability limits and
- overbreak in rock excavation.

Tenderers will then be able to tender on a common basis, knowing that they must allow in their pricing for the occurrence of physical conditions within the stated boundary limits.

Adverse weather 60.1 (13)

Rather than rely on the subjective generalisations about 'exceptionally inclement weather' sometimes included in standard forms of contract, the ECC includes a more objective and measurable approach. The purpose is to make available for each contract *weather data*, compiled by an independent authority and agreed by both Parties beforehand, establishing the levels of selected relevant weather conditions for the Site for each calendar month which have had a period of return of more than ten years. If weather conditions more adverse than these levels occur it is a compensation event. Weather which the *weather data* show is likely to occur within a ten year period is the *Contractor*'s risk in relation to both cost and time.

The time of occurrence of all compensation events is when the action or lack of action describing the event in Clause 60.1 takes place. In the case of weather it is the day when the stated test shows that weather conditions are recorded as having occurred within a calendar month which 'do not occur on average less frequently than once in ten years'. The test is the comparison of the *weather measurements* with the *weather data*. The compensation event can then be notified under Clause 61.3 and its effect can be assessed at the end of the month when the extent of the weather exceeding the ten year return *weather data* is known. The process starts again at the beginning of each month.

This compensation event is concerned with weather occurring only at the place stated in the Contract Data. If weather occurring at some distance from the Site could produce some risk such as flooding on the Site, the allocation of risk should be dealt with by special compensation events, such as the second example in the introductory notes on Clause 60.

Weather characteristics for extended construction sites, such as cross country pipelines, may vary considerably along the length of the Site. In such cases the Site should be divided into areas, each chosen to have reasonably uniform weather characteristics throughout the area. Appropriate *weather measurements* and *weather data* can then be used for each area.

The provisions for weather in the ECC have been developed in consultation with the United Kingdom Meteorological Office (the Met Office) which can provide advice and information about the availability of recorded *weather data*. The addresses and telephone numbers of the offices to be contacted are given in the Met Office notice reproduced in Appendix 6. There is a charge for providing data.

In most of the more populous parts of the United Kingdom, there is sufficient coverage of Met Office weather stations to be able to relate to any particular site. The Met Office is also able to advise on methods of recording the actual *weather measurements*. In some cases, measurements taken at a neighbouring weather station will be sufficiently representative of the weather on the Site.

The Met Office can also advise on expected weather conditions on sites outside the United Kingdom and, if necessary, recommend a meteorological authority to provide the *weather data*. Many countries have authorities similar to the Met Office where similar data is available. In other countries there may be little established data but it may still be possible, with the advice of the appropriate weather authority, to agree limiting values approximating to the 'once in ten year' average. This would provide an adequate basis for an adverse weather compensation event. Where no recorded data are available, the assumed *weather data* is entered in the Contract Data.

Weather parameters

The choice of weather measurements depends upon the types of construction operation to be carried out and the weather characteristics of the area.

Clause 60.1(13) refers to the *weather measurements*. Part one of the Contract Data includes four measurements for which 10 year 'return period statistics' for each calendar month may be required. Met Office data are recorded by calendar month. These measurements have been selected as being the minimum weather aspects which can have a significant effect on construction work in the United Kingdom and countries with similar climates. They are

- the cumulative rainfall (mm) (this includes the equivalent rainfall corresponding to falls of snow)
- the number of days with rainfall more than 5 mm (a measure of the days when outside work may be interrupted by rain),
- the number of days with minimum air temperature less than 0 degrees Celsius, and
- the number of days with snow lying at a stated time GMT (in the United Kingdom, Met Office readings are taken at 0900 hours GMT; the time may vary in other countries).

Space is left in the Contract Data part one for adding other measurements pertinent to the Site in question or the operations to be carried out. For instance, if tower cranes are to be used, a reference to the number of working hours or days in a month in which the wind speed exceeds a critical level may be appropriate. The actual wind speed at the Site would need to be related to the speed at the reference weather station. The Met Office or local weather authority should be consulted about the practicality of additional measurements.

Weather records during the contract

The data routinely recorded at a weather station close to the Site could be used as an alternative to recording on the Site. If there is not a weather station nearby, the *weather measurements* should be made using gauges and equipment installed at the place stated in the Contract Data.

Employer's risk events 60.1 (14)

The *Employer*'s risks are stated in Clause 80.1. Any additional *Employer*'s risks should be stated in part one of the Contract Data.

Employer's use of the works 60.1 (15)

The *Employer* may use a part of the *works* before Completion and, unless the use is for the reasons stated in Clause 35.3, he takes over that part. If take over occurs before the Completion Date, it is a compensation event.

It is therefore important that the Works Information should state the reasons why the *Employer* may require to use parts of the *works* before Completion. For instance he may require access across parts of the *works* for his own purposes.

Alternatively, the *Contractor* may request the *Employer* to use part of the *works* to suit the *Contractor*'s method of working.

Under Clause 35.3, take over would not occur in either of these circumstances and there would be no compensation event.

Materials, facilities, etc. for tests 60.1 (16)

Under Clause 40.2, the *Employer* is required to provide materials, facilities and samples for tests as stated in the Works Information.

Assumptions about compensation events 60.1 (17)

Under Clause 61.6 (see later notes) the *Project Manager* may state assumptions to be used in the assessment of a compensation event. If he later notifies corrections to such assumptions, the notification is a separate compensation event.

Employer's breach of contract 60.1 (18)

This is an 'umbrella' clause to include breaches of contract by the *Employer* within the compensation event procedure.

Notifying compensation events 61

61.1 This procedure would normally apply to compensation events 1, 4, 7, 8, 10, 15 and 17 each of which is due to an action by the *Project Manager* or *Supervisor*. When the event occurs, the *Project Manager* notifies the *Contractor* and instructs him to submit quotations. Where the compensation event results from the *Contractor*'s fault or where quotations have already been submitted, quotations are not instructed. However, in order to avoid doubt in such cases, it is advisable that when the *Project Manager* notifies the compensation event, he should give his reason for not instructing quotations. The *Contractor* is required to act on the instruction or changed decision.

61.2 This clause deals with the situation where the *Project Manager* is considering issuing an instruction or changing a decision but first requires to know what effect this would have on cost and Completion (for example, when he is considering a change to the Works Information (Clause 60.1(1))). He has the authority to instruct the *Contractor* to submit quotations as a first step.

61.3 This procedure would normally apply to the compensation events not covered by those in Clause 61.1. These are events which arise from

- a failure by the *Employer*, *Project Manager*, or *Supervisor* or Others to fulfil their obligations (compensation events 2, 3, 5, 6, 11, 16 and 18),
- the *Project Manager* withholding an acceptance for a reason not stated in the contract (compensation event 9) or
- a happening not caused by any party (compensation events 12 and 13).

It would also apply to an event which the *Project Manager* has not notified under Clause 61.1.

In such cases, the *Contractor* initiates the procedure by notifying the *Project Manager*. The stated time limit is intended to expedite the procedure so that dealing with compensation events a long time after they have occurred is avoided.

61.4 This clause lists the four tests which the *Project Manager* applies to an event notified by the *Contractor* in order to decide whether or not to instruct the *Contractor* to submit quotations for its effect. If the *Project Manager* decides that the event does not pass any one of the tests he notifies the *Contractor* and no further action is required unless the *Contractor* disputes the decision and refers it to the *Adjudicator* under Clause 90.1.

In many circumstances, the *Project Manager* will be able to give his decision within a week of the *Contractor*'s notification. With more complicated events, a longer period will be desirable to ensure adequate time for a properly considered decision. Provision is made for such longer periods subject to the *Contractor*'s agreement.

61.5 The *Project Manager* should include in an instruction to submit quotations his decision on whether or not the *Contractor* gave an early warning which an experienced contractor could have given.

61.6 In some cases, the nature of the compensation event may be such that it is impossible to prepare a sufficiently accurate quotation. One example of this is where unexpected physical conditions are encountered (compensation event 12) but their extent is unknown. In these cases, quotations are submitted on the basis of assumptions stated by the *Project Manager* in his instruction to the *Contractor*. If the assumptions later prove to be wrong, the *Project Manager*'s notification of their correction is a separate compensation event (Clause 60.1(17)).

Apart from this situation, the assessment of compensation events cannot be revised (Clause 65.2). The reason for this strict procedure is to motivate the parties to decide the effects of each compensation event either before or soon after it occurs. Since each quotation can include due allowance for risk (Clause 63.5), and the early warning procedure should minimise the effects of unexpected problems, the need for later review is minimal.

Quotations for compensation events 62

62.1 There may be several ways of adjusting plans for the work to deal with a compensation event and its consequences. The procedure in this clause enables the *Project Manager* to consider different options. For instance, it may be more beneficial to the *Employer* to achieve earlier Completion at a greater cost than an alternative of later Completion at a lower cost. The clause also provides for the *Contractor* to submit quotations using methods other than those assumed in the *Project Manager*'s instruction. For instance, the *Contractor* may be able to use a specialised item of Equipment, the availability of which the *Project Manager* was unaware.

In the Options C, D, E and F, the *Contractor*'s cost of preparing quotations for compensation events will usually be included in Actual Cost, as defined for the main option being used and thus in PWDD.

In the priced options A and B, the cost of preparing quotations for compensation events is specifically excluded from Actual Cost (Clause 11.2(28)). Tenderers should therefore allow in their tendered *fee percentage* for such costs as they are not reimbursed directly.

This policy has been adopted in options A and B in order to retain the certainty of the Prices relative to the work done. However, some *Employers* are making special arrangements to reimburse costs of preparing quotations in particular circumstances, for example:

- when the effect is very large;
- when the *Employer* is asking for multiple quotations for significant design changes, especially when different options are being considered.

62.2 Quotations comprise a 'package' of time and money as, in most situations, it is impossible to consider either in isolation. The use of the term 'quotations' is not the same as the normal use in commerce, i.e. the free submission of an offer. Quotations are based on an assessment of forecast or recorded Actual Cost (Clause 63.1) and time (Clause 63.3) arising from the compensation event. A build-up of each quotation is required to be submitted by the *Contractor*. If re-programming of remaining work is affected, the quotation should include a revised programme, showing, amongst other things, any change to planned Completion and the Completion Date.

62.3 The time limits are intended to promote efficient management of the contract procedures. The time limits for submission and for the *Project Manager*'s reply may, however, be extended under certain conditions as stated in Clause 62.5. An example of the need for this flexibility is when a weather compensation event (Clause 60.1(13)) occurs very early in a calendar month. The effect of the event cannot be assessed until the end of the month when the extent of the weather exceeding the ten year return *weather data* becomes known. If the event is notified by both the *Contractor* and the *Project Manager* immediately, the time remaining to the end of the month may be more than the three weeks allowed for the *Contractor* to quote. An extension of the time to quote would then be necessary.

The four categories of reply by the *Project Manager* are listed. The third category may result from the *Project Manager* deciding not to proceed with a proposed change to the Works Information. This is likely to happen when the cost of the change is too high or the delay too great. The *Project Manager* has absolute discretion in such a case on whether to proceed.

62.4 This procedure permits revision of quotations. In practice, this will usually follow discussion between the *Project Manager* and the *Contractor* on the details of the submitted quotations. Again, time limits for submission of the revised quotation are stated.

62.5 This clause provides for the extension of the time limits stated in Clause 62.3 which may be necessary with the more complicated events. The *Project Manager* and the *Contractor* must agree to the extension before the expiry of the times stated.

A similar clause is included in the EC Subcontract. However, if a compensation event in a subcontract affects a main contract compensation event, the *Contractor* should not agree to extend time limits in the subcontract unless he has obtained the *Project Manager*'s agreement to an appropriate extension in the main contract.

Assessing compensation events **63**

63.1 Assessment of compensation events as they affect Prices is based on their effect on Actual Cost plus the Fee. This is different from some standard forms where variations are valued using the rates and prices in the contract as a basis. The reason for this policy is that no compensation event for which a quotation is required is due to the fault of the *Contractor* or relates to a matter which is at his risk under the contract. It is therefore appropriate to reimburse the *Contractor* his forecast additional costs or actual additional costs if work has already been done arising from the compensation event. Disputes arising from the applicability of contract rates are avoided.

Usually the assessment will be the forecast of Actual Cost of work which is yet to be done but it may include an element of achieved Actual Cost for work which has been done (e.g. when an emergency instruction has had to be given).

Where the work to be done is changed, it is important that the assessment is based upon the change in forecast or recorded Actual Cost. The clause gives no authority for the price for the originally specified work to be deleted and for the forecast Actual Cost of all work now required to be used as the basis for a new price.

If the Works Information originally included a piece of work (a) which is now to be replaced by a piece of work (b), the compensation is assessed as the difference between the forecast Actual Cost of (b) and the forecast Actual Cost of (a). The Fee is then added to this difference and the resulting total amount is used to change the Prices. The original price for (a) does not enter the assessment. There is no authority in the clause or elsewhere in the ECC for assessing the compensation event as the forecast Actual Cost of (b) plus the Fee minus the original price for (a).

Similarly, if the effect of a compensation event is only to delete future work, the assessment is based on the forecast Actual Cost of that work plus the Fee, not simply a deletion of the price for the deleted work. There is, of course, no obstruction to the *Project Manager* and the *Contractor* agreeing to delete the price if both are satisfied that it adequately represents the reduction in forecast Actual Cost plus the Fee.

If some or all the work arising from a compensation event has already been done, Actual Cost should be readily assessable from records. Forecasting future Actual Cost is less straightforward. Estimates of resources are required and productivity rates for Equipment and labour. Except for Option F, pricing of the various components of Actual Cost is based on the Schedule of Cost Components with the associated percentages tendered in the Contract Data part two. Where there is a large number of compensation events, the Shorter SCC should be particularly useful. The Fee is calculated in accordance with Clause 11.2(17).

63.2 The only compensation events in Clause 60.1 which allow a reduction of the Prices (if the assessment shows a reduction in Actual Cost plus the Fee) are a change to the Works Information (Clause 60.1(1)) and the correction of an assumption made in assessing an earlier compensation event under Clause 61.6 (Clause 60.1(17)).

The only compensation events in the optional clauses which allow a reduction of the Prices are those arising from Clauses 60.4 and 60.6 in options B and D and from secondary option Clause T1.1. All other compensation events listed in Clause 60.1 and in the optional clauses cannot lead to reduced Prices even if their effect is to reduce Actual Cost plus Fee.

There is provision, however, for additional compensation events to be included in the Contract Data. Such an additional compensation event can only lead to increased or unchanged Prices unless an additional condition, using Option Z, states specifically that it can also lead to reduced prices.

63.3 No compensation event can result in a reduction in the time for carrying out the *works*, i.e. an earlier Completion Date. Only an acceleration as agreed under Clause 36 can result in an earlier Completion Date.

The first stage in assessing whether the Completion Date should be delayed as a result of a compensation event is to adjust the Accepted Programme to take account of the compensation event with any appropriate adjustments to time risk allowances (Clause 63.5). Any float in the programme before planned Completion is available to mitigate or avoid any consequential delay to planned Completion (see notes on Clause 31.2). If planned Completion is delayed, the Completion Date is delayed by the same period. If planned Completion is not delayed, the Completion Date is unchanged.

63.4 The *Contractor*'s duty to give an early warning is stated in Clause 16.1. The sanction if the *Contractor* fails to give early warning is stated in this clause. It is possible that early warning could have allowed actions to be taken which would have reduced costs and saved time. It is important that the *Project Manager* notifies the *Contractor* of his decision that early warning should have been given (Clause 61.5) so that the *Contractor* knows the correct basis for his assessment and the nature of the early warning.

63.5 Allowances for risk must be included in forecasts of Actual Cost and Completion in the same way that the *Contractor* allows for risks when pricing his tender. The value of the allowance is greater when the work is uncertain and there is a high chance of a *Contractor*'s risk happening. It is least when the uncertainties are small and when the work is to be done by resources already on Site whose output rates can be predicted relatively accurately.

63.6 This clause protects the *Employer* against inefficiency on the part of the *Contractor*. The reference to changing the Accepted Programme is made so that it is clear that the *Contractor* is expected to alter his arrangements when necessary.

63.7 This clause expresses the 'contra proferentem' rule which interprets a clause containing an ambiguity or inconsistency against the party responsible for drafting the document in which it occurs.

The *Project Manager*'s assessments 64

64.1 The four circumstances in which the *Project Manager* assesses a compensation event are stated. They are all derived from some failure of the *Contractor*. The second results from the *Contractor* not assessing the compensation event correctly in accordance with the contract. This means that the changes to the Prices have not been correctly assessed in accordance with Clause 63.1 and/or the change to the Completion Date has not been correctly assessed in accordance with Clause 63.3. The third and fourth circumstances are derived from the need to base an assessment on an Accepted Programme which has been revised as required by Clause 32. The *Project Manager* will be motivated to make a fair and reasonable assessment in the knowledge that the *Contractor* may refer the matter to the *Adjudicator*, who may change the assessment.

64.2 If the Accepted Programme is non-existent or has not been revised as required in Clause 32, the *Project Manager* is required to carry out his own assessment of the programme for the remaining work. This is a major incentive on the *Contractor* to keep his programme up to date.

64.3 This clause provides for the *Project Manager* to have the same time to make his assessment as the *Contractor* was allowed for his.

Implementing compensation events 65

65.1 This clause should be read in conjunction with Clause 65.4 for options A, B, C and D and Clause 65.3 for options E and F. Implementation is by the *Project Manager* changing the Prices and the Completion Date in accordance with the assessment of which he has notified the *Contractor*.

65.2 This clause emphasises the finality of the assessment of compensation events. If the records of resources on work actually carried out show that achieved Actual Cost and timing are different from the forecasts included in the accepted quotation or in the *Project Manager*'s assessment, the assessment is not changed. The only circumstances in which a review is possible are those stated in Clause 61.6.

MAIN OPTION CLAUSES

Option A: Priced contract with activity schedule

Assessing compensation events 63

63.8 The changed *activity schedule* (Clause 11.2(20)) which takes account of the effect of the compensation event is used for subsequent assessments of the PWDD.

63.10 This clause covers the assessment of compensation events for work which involves a Subcontractor. The effect of this clause is that only the Fee tendered by the *Contractor* will be applied to the assessment of Actual Cost for the compensation event. There are two reasons why the clause is designed in this way; firstly to avoid the *Employer* paying two sets of fees on work which is subcontracted and secondly because the *Employer* has no control over Fees tendered by subcontractors.

It is recognised that, on subcontracted work, the *Contractor* will incur administrative costs and is entitled to receive a contribution towards these costs. This will be achieved by the *Contractor* ensuring that the Fee accepted at the award of a subcontract is within his main contract allowances.

Subcontractors tendering under the NEC Engineering and Construction Subcontract should not include overheads relating to manufacture and fabrication outside the Working Areas in their tendered Fee. These overheads should be included in the percentage tendered in part two of the Contract Data for manufacturing and fabrication overheads for use in the assessment of Actual Cost under Section 52 of the Schedule of Cost Components.

Contractors who wish to secure an appropriate contribution to their overheads from compensation events affecting subcontract work, should pay attention to the split between the percentages tendered by subcontractors for the Fee and for the manufacturing and fabrication overheads in Section 52 of the SCC.

63.11 The Shorter SCC should be useful where there is a large number of small compensation events.

Implementing compensation events **65**

65.4 See notes on core Clauses 65.1.

Option B: Priced contract with bill of quantities

Compensation events **60**

60.4 A change in quantity is not, in itself, a compensation event. A compensation event is triggered only by the changed quantity satisfying the two tests stated in the clause.

This clause only applies to changes in quantities which do not result from changes to the Works Information. A change to the Works Information is always a compensation event, subject to the exceptions in Clause 60.1(1), regardless of the effect on quantities.

60.5 A difference between original and final quantities in a *bill of quantities* is not, in itself, a compensation event. The amount due to the *Contractor* includes the PWDD which is based on the actual quantities of work done. However, any difference of quantities which causes Completion to be delayed is a compensation event.

60.6 There may be mistakes in the *bill of quantities* because the bill does not comply with the *method of measurement* or because of ambiguities or inconsistencies. This may occur where an item has been omitted from the bill or an item in the bill should be deleted or amended to comply with the *method of measurement*. This is one of the compensation events which may result in a reduction of the Prices.

Assessing compensation events **63**

63.9 The *bill of quantities* will require amendment in the form of deletion, addition or revision of quantities or items or rates and lump sums. The changed *bill of quantities* (Clause 11.2(21)) which takes account of the effect of the compensation event is used for subsequent assessments of the PWDD.

Subject to agreement, the rates and lump sums in the *bill of quantities* may be used for assessing compensation events instead of building up the Actual Cost of each item of work using the Schedule of Cost Components and then adding the Fee. This may apply particularly for small items, where calculations using the

Schedule of Cost Components may be unduly lengthy in relation to the value of the compensation event. This method assumes that the rates and prices in the *bill of quantities* are equivalent to Actual Cost plus the Fee.

63.10 This clause covers the assessment of compensation events for work which involves a Subcontractor. The effect of this clause is that only the Fee tendered by the *Contractor* will be applied to the assessment of Actual Cost for the compensation event. There are two reasons why the clause is designed in this way; firstly to avoid the *Employer* paying two sets of fees on work which is subcontracted and secondly because the *Employer* has no control over Fees tendered by subcontractors.

It is recognised that, on subcontracted work, the *Contractor* will incur administrative costs and is entitled to receive a contribution towards these costs. This will be achieved if the *Contractor* ensures that the Fee accepted at the award of a subcontract is within his main contract allowances.

Subcontractors tendering under the NEC Engineering and Construction Subcontract should not include overheads relating to manufacture and fabrication outside the Working Areas in their tendered Fee. These overheads should be included in the percentage tendered in part two of the Contract Data for manufacturing and fabrication overheads for use in the assessment of Actual Cost under Section 52 of the Schedule of Cost Components.

Main contractors who wish to secure an appropriate contribution to their overheads from compensation events affecting subcontract work should pay attention to the split between the percentages tendered by subcontractors for the Fee and for the manufacturing and fabrication overheads in Section 52 of the SCC.

63.11 The Shorter SCC should be useful where there is a large number of small compensation events.

Implementing compensation events **65**

65.4 See notes on core Clause 65.1.

Option C: Target contract with activity schedule

Assessing compensation events **63**

63.8 The changed *activity schedule* (Clause 11.2(20)), which takes account of the effect of the compensation event is used for the subsequent calculation of the *Contractor*'s share.

63.11 The Shorter SCC should be useful where there is a large number of small compensation events.

Implementing compensation events **65**

65.4 See notes on core Clause 65.1.

Option D: Target contract with bill of quantities

Compensation events **60**

60.4 A change in quantity is not, in itself, a compensation event. A compensation event is triggered only by the changed quantity satisfying the two tests stated in the clause.

This clause only applies to changes in quantities which do not result from changes to the Works Information. A change to the Works Information is always a compensation event, subject to the exceptions in Clause 60.1(1), regardless of the effect on quantities.

60.5 A difference between original and final quantities in a *bill of quantities* is not, in itself, a compensation event. The amount due to the *Contractor* includes the PWDD which is based on the actual quantities of work done. However, any difference of quantities which causes Completion to be delayed is a compensation event.

60.6 There may be mistakes in the *bill of quantities*, because the bill does not comply with the *method of measurement*, or because of ambiguities or inconsistencies. This may occur where an item has been omitted from the bill or an item in the bill should be deleted or amended to comply with the *method of measurement*. This is one of the compensation events which may result in a reduction of the Prices.

Assessing compensation events 63

63.9 The *bill of quantities* will require amendment in the form of deletion, addition or revision of quantities or items or rates and lump sums. The changed *bill of quantities* (Clause 11.2(21)) which takes account of the effect of the compensation event is used for the subsequent calculation of the *Contractor*'s share.

Subject to agreement, the rates and lump sums in the *bill of quantities* may be used for assessing compensation events instead of building up the Actual Cost of each item of work using the Schedule of Cost Components and then adding the Fee. This may apply particularly for small items, where calculations using the Schedule of Cost Components may be unduly lengthy in relation to the value of the compensation event. This method assumes that the rates and prices in the *bill of quantities* are equivalent to Actual Cost plus the Fee.

63.11 The Shorter SCC should be useful where there is a large number of small compensation events.

Implementing compensation events 65

65.4 See notes on core Clause 65.1

Option E: Cost reimbursable contract

Assessing compensation events 63

63.11 The Shorter SCC should be useful where there is a large number of small compensation events.

Implementing compensation events 65

65.3 See notes on core Clause 65.1.

65.5 This clause enables the *Project Manager* to choose between alternative ways of dealing with a compensation event arising in a subcontract before the *Contractor* instructs the Subcontractor.

Option F:Management contract

Implementing compensation events 65

65.3 See notes on core Clause 65.1.

65.5 This clause enables the *Project Manager* to choose between alternative ways of dealing with a compensation event arising in a subcontract before the *Contractor* instructs the Subcontractor.

7 Title

CORE CLAUSES

For large, expensive or important items of Equipment, Plant or Materials which are being manufactured or stored outside the Working Areas, the *Employer* is advised to secure ownership and at the same time make payment to the *Contractor*. Under Clause 71.1, the *Supervisor* marks such items if the contract identifies them for payment and the *Contractor* has prepared them for marking as required. There are, in consequence, several important procedural steps which need to be taken.

- The Works Information must identify the items as being subject to marking under this Section and, other documents such as the *bills of quantities*, *activity schedules* should show them individually and separately.
- The *Contractor* must prepare the items for marking as required by the Works Information and the *Supervisor* must ensure that these requirements are met.
- The *Supervisor* is obliged to mark the items if the criteria of the Works Information have been met.

The requirements in the Works Information for marking should state that as part of preparing the items, the *Contractor* has to show title and only after demonstration of such title will marking and payment follow. The *Supervisor* must check the title before marking.

The *Employer*'s title to Equipment, Plant and Materials **70**

70.1 Upon the marking of the particular item of Equipment, Plant or Materials, as separately identified, title passes to the *Employer*. For further comment on Equipment purchased by the *Contractor* under hire purchase or a lease agreement, see notes on SCC 22(b).

70.2 Before the *Contractor* removes any items of Equipment, Plant or Materials (including surpluses, unusable or defective goods) he must obtain the *Project Manager*'s written permission to effect such removal. Not to do so means the items may remain in the title of the *Employer* and hence could cause considerable complications for the *Contractor* especially if Plant and Materials are returned to suppliers or Equipment is delivered to another contract. It would normally be advisable for the *Contractor* and the *Project Manager* to agree a simple procedure in order to facilitate normal movement of resources in and out of the Working Areas.

Marking Equipment, Plant and Materials outside the Working Areas **71**

71.1 If the procedures necessary prior to marking having been completed to the *Supervisor*'s satisfaction, he has a duty to mark any Equipment, Plant and Materials outside the Working Areas which are stated in the contract to be paid for before being delivered to Working Areas. The contract (ie. the Works Information, *activity schedule* or *bills of quantities*) must identify the items for which payment may become due.

Removing Equipment **72**

72.1 This clause places an obligation on the *Contractor* to remove Equipment from the Site when it is no longer needed. It may, however, be permitted to remain on the Site either temporarily or permanently if the *Project Manager* allows. Examples are temporary storage of items of Equipment pending transfer to another site and temporary sheet piling or formwork which the *Contractor* may not wish to recover. Items such as the latter, however, remain as Equipment left in the *works* and do not become part of the *works*.

Objects and materials within the Site **73**

73.1 This clause establishes that the *Contractor* has no title to objects of value or of historical or other interest within the Site. Title to such objects may belong to the *Employer* or some other party. Any instructions to deal with such objects issued by the *Project Manager*, such as removal to the *Employer*'s store, is a compensation event under Clause 60.1(7).

73.2 The Works Information should state which materials from excavation and demolition are to be the property of the *Contractor* and any conditions regarding their removal from the Site.

The Works Information should state also how the *Contractor* is to deal with known items of value in property to be demolished or elsewhere on the Site and appropriate items included in the *activity schedule* or *bill of quantities* (if any).

8 Risks and insurance

CORE CLAUSES

It is important to recognise the distinction between the various types of risk and which party bears them. Risks of loss of or physical damage to property or of personal injury or death, which are usually insurable risks, are quite separate from general, legal or financial risks.

This Risks and insurance Section 8 deals with the general, legal and the insurable risks of loss, damage, injury or death and what insurances are required to cover them. The risks which could result in loss, damage, injury or death, if they happen, are allocated to either the *Employer* or the *Contractor*.

Financial risks are dealt with in other parts of the contract, such as under the compensation event procedure in Section 6. For example, the *Employer* carries the financial risk for additional work instructed under Clause 60.1(1) but the risk in carrying it out remains with the *Contractor*.

On the other hand the *Contractor* carries the financial risk of doing work which he has priced in the contract including the insurance requirements under Clause 84.1.

Employer's risks 80

80.1 The *Employer*'s risks are stated in Clause 80.1. There are six main categories of *Employer*'s risks.

The first is the *Employer*'s risks relating to his use of the Site or *works*, his own general or legal responsibilities and faults in his design. For liabilities which might arise from design faults the *Employer* should either insure the risk by a professional indemnity policy if the design is by his own resources or ensure that it is covered (e.g. under the NEC Professional Services Contract) if an external consultant is engaged to do the design work.

The second category relating to items supplied to the *Contractor* is at the risk of the *Employer* up to the point of their hand-over to the *Contractor* or a Subcontractor. Any insurance cover for these should be either under the *Employer*'s own loss or damage policy or the insurances of Others (as defined in Clause 11.2(2)) until the *Contractor* or Subcontractor has received and accepted the Plant and Materials concerned.

The third category of *Employer*'s risk is the loss of or damage to the *works*, Plant and Materials caused by outside influences beyond the control of the Parties. This risk is limited to what can be regarded as the *Employer*'s property. The *Contractor* carries the risk of loss of or damage to his property from any of these causes.

The fourth category of *Employer*'s risk is that arising once he has assumed responsibility (i.e. taken over under Clause 35) for any part of the *works*. Upon this happening, the *Employer* takes on the consequences of normal ownership and should insure his asset in the usual way if he so wishes. There are some important risks which, even after takeover, remain with the *Contractor* but these are likely to be small and disappear with the issue of the Defects Certificate.

The fifth category of *Employer*'s risk is that of loss of or damage to the *works* and any Equipment, Plant and Materials retained on the Site after termination.

The last category of the *Employer*'s risks provides for him to carry additional risks. These must be clearly stated in the Contract Data. An important example of where the *Employer* might wish to carry an additional risk or limit the *Contractor*'s risk is when the *works* are within an existing plant or facility of the *Employer*.

In a refinery it is quite usual for the *Employer* to retain all or most of the risk of loss or damage to his property which surrounds the *works* being carried out. In this case the *Contractor* would see from the Contract Data part one to what extent the *Employer* has retained this risk and hence what residual risk he has to insure under the Insurance Table third item. If the *Contractor* and the *Employer*, in effect, share a risk then the *Contractor* must ensure that his insurances are adequate at least up to the limit of his risk.

Another example would be for equipment made available to the *Contractor* by the *Employer* for which the *Employer* preferred to retain direct control and hence risk. A vital distinction must then be recognised between the equipment which concerns the *Employer* and the Equipment (note the capital 'E' for Equipment in the second classification of insurance in the Insurance Table) as defined in Clause 11.2(11). Thus the risk of loss of or damage to equipment under this example is an *Employer*'s risk but loss of or damage to defined Equipment is a *Contractor*'s risk.

The *Contractor*'s risks 81

81.1 The *Contractor*'s risks are defined as all the risks which are not identified in Clause 80.1 as being carried by the *Employer*. The *Contractor*'s risks include those as stated in the insurance clauses even when such risk is covered by insurance procured by the *Employer*. This aspect is explained more fully in the notes for Clause 87.2.

Repairs 82

82.1 The *Contractor* is required to carry out all works of repair until the Defects Certificate has been issued. Consequently, unless otherwise instructed by the *Project Manager*, this will include repairs arising from an *Employer*'s risk event such as damage to the *works* after take over but before the Defects Certificate. The *Project Manager* must decide how to deal with loss or damage caused by an *Employer*'s risk event. It is possible that, in certain circumstances, he decides the damage should not be repaired. In such a case he would issue instructions to the *Contractor*, who will then neither be obliged to carry out such repair work nor be entitled to receive any compensation.

Indemnity 83

83.1 Under this clause each party indemnifies the other for events which are at his risk.

83.2 Provision is made for the liability of a Party to be reduced on a proportional basis if events at the risk of the other Party contributed to the event.

Insurance cover 84

84.1 This clause requires the *Contractor* to take out insurance cover. Major multi-discipline employers may prefer to arrange all or some of this insurance themselves, in view of the large number and size of contracts in which they invest. In such cases, insurers are likely to take a much greater interest in the running of the contract as the *Contractor* is no longer motivated to minimise claims. If the *Employer* wishes to effect his own insurance, the details should be given in the Contract Data. Otherwise, the events and extent of cover to be effected by the *Contractor* are as shown in the Insurance Table and detailed in the Contract Data.

The *works* and Equipment would normally be insured under a Contractor's All Risks (CAR) policy. Since the value of the *works* constructed will increase as the contract progresses, either the insured sum should be updated, at intervals, or alternatively the policy should recognise such increase as being automatically covered. Insurance of the *works* and Equipment covers only the *Contractor*'s risks. It is for the *Employer* to decide whether or not he wishes to take out insurance cover for his own risks. It is important in all cases to check that the terms of any standard policy comply with the requirements of the contract.

Insurance of the *works*, Equipment, and Plant and Materials is on a value indemnity basis. This is particularly relevant to insurance of Equipment as it means that cover is for replacement with equipment of similar age and condition rather than on a 'new-for-old' basis.

With regard to the fourth event in the Insurance Table, employers in many countries are required by law to insure employees for personal injury and death.

84.2 The *Project Manager* and the *Contractor* must ensure that the policies and certificates are in the joint names of the *Employer* and the *Contractor* including for those insurances procured by the *Employer* for those matters at the *Contractor*'s risk.

Insurance policies 85

85.1 The *Project Manager* should satisfy himself that the terms of the insurance policies satisfy the contract requirements and that the *Employer*'s interests are adequately protected.

85.2 The purpose of waiver of subrogation rights is to prevent insurers taking action against the *Employer*'s personnel, for example, after having paid money to the *Contractor* in settlement of a claim by him.

85.3 The Parties must comply with the terms of the insurance policies as not so to do may make the insurance partially or fully void and incur the Parties in substantial risk.

85.4 Careful consideration should be given by the *Employer* and the *Contractor* to the amounts for deductibles. Deductibles, sometimes known as excesses, represent the amount of liability retained by the insured. By this means, the insured shares the exposure to risk with the insurer.

The amount of the deductible affects the level of premium which the insured must pay. Reasons for applying deductibles in insurance policies include

- decrease in level of premiums,
- elimination of administration costs of processing a large number of small claims,
- involving the insured in retaining some liability by sharing the risks and thus encouraging him to take more care in avoiding loss or damage, and
- reducing the risk assumed by the insurer to a limit which he can bear.

Employers who enter 'nil' against the deductibles in the Contract Data are likely to pay very high level premiums.

If the *Contractor* does not insure 86

86.1 This clause enables the *Employer* to take out the relevant insurances in the event that the *Contractor* fails to do so at the time and for the periods stated in the contract. Appropriate adjustments are then made to the amounts certified by the *Project Manager*.

Insurance by the *Employer* 87

87.1 In certain circumstances it may be more appropriate and convenient for the Employer to effect some of the joint name insurances which, under the standard conditions, are to be taken out by the Contractor. The Contractor is required to accept the policies and certificates, in the same way that the Employer is required to do so for insurances effected by the *Contractor*.

87.2 Whilst the *Contractor* is entitled to rely upon the *Employer* providing the insurances as stated in the Contract Data, it is important that the *Contractor* recognises that his risks include those shown in the Insurance Table. Consequently, even if such insurances are effected by the *Employer*, the *Contractor* should satisfy himself as to the adequacy of the policy and cover. The *Contractor* should inform the *Project Manager* of any discrepancy between the *Employer* — provided insurances as stated in the Contract Data and the *Employer* — provided insurances as actually given and ask for a policy amendment.

87.3 If the *Employer*

- fails to effect the insurances which the Contract Data states he is to provide or
- provides insurances which do not comply with the Contract Data

the *Contractor* may procure additional insurance to top up any shortfall he considers exists in these insurances. The *Employer* will then either pay the insurers directly or the *Contractor* will be reimbursed.

9 Disputes and termination

CORE CLAUSES

This section describes the procedures for dealing with disputes and the circumstances under which the Parties may terminate the contract and the subsequent procedures.

The only means of dispute resolution in many forms of contract is arbitration or litigation which in recent years have become both time consuming and expensive. Whilst the NEC system recognises the need to have an ultimate means for such resolution, an intermediate stage of independent dispute resolution has been introduced in the form of adjudication. It is the intention that all disputes should be resolved by the *Adjudicator* who is appointed jointly by the *Employer* and the *Contractor* and is able to act independently. However, any Party dissatisfied with the *Adjudicator*'s decision may refer the dispute to the *tribunal*.

A feature of the ECC is that the *Employer* is given a choice of tribunal and hence is required in the Contract Data to insert his choice, e.g. arbitration, expert determination, a disputes resolution panel or the courts. However, if arbitration is available under the *law of the contract* (Clause 12.2) it is strongly recommended that arbitration is chosen as the *tribunal*. The rationale for arbitration remains important particularly for disputes upon technical matters for which an arbitrator experienced in the technical context of the dispute is preferable to the courts. (See further notes under Clause 93.2.)

Settlement of disputes 90

90.1 Whereas the first item in the table deals with a disputed action of the *Project Manager* or *Supervisor*, the second item deals with lack of action. The third item deals with all other disputes.

An action may be, for example

- an instruction,
- an acceptance, non-acceptance or rejection,
- a certification,
- an assessment,
- a notification,
- a decision.

Each instruction, acceptance, non-acceptance, rejection, certification, assessment, notice or decision is a separate action.

In the event of a dispute on an action or lack of action, the dispute may be, for example

- an action which should not have been taken,
- the lack of an action which should have been taken,
- an action taken outside the specified time limits,
- an action which is incomplete or ill-judged,
- an action which is an assessment improperly made or incorrectly calculated,
- an action taken without authority.

All disputes of whatever kind are first dealt with by adjudication. Only if either Party is dissatisfied with the *Adjudicator*'s decision will it be taken further. For a general matter in dispute, either Party may submit it to the *Adjudicator* but for matters concerning an action or lack of action by the *Project Manager* or *Supervisor* only the *Contractor* is permitted to submit it to the *Adjudicator*. This is because at all times the *Project Manager* and *Supervisor* are acting on behalf of the *Employer*.

Adjudication is not arbitration. It is a means by which an independent third party makes a quick decision where the Parties are unable to agree.

Time stipulations are clearly set out in the table and throughout the disputes procedure in order to avoid protracted exchanges and argument and to achieve prompt resolution of disputes.

The initial period of two weeks after the *Contractor*'s notification gives the *Project Manager* or *Supervisor* the opportunity to take or amend the action. This period of grace is intended to prevent the *Adjudicator* becoming involved with matters which may have been overlooked.

The decision of the *Adjudicator* may simply be that the *Project Manager* or *Supervisor* should have acted or should not have acted, but in certain circumstances he may also decide what action should have been taken. In the cases in which he decides that the *Project Manager* or *Supervisor* acted or did not act in accordance with the contract or in any other matter which he decides in the *Contractor*'s favour, he assesses both financial and time effects.

90.2 No details are given in the clause of how the decision and the associated reasons are to be drafted. However, the essential requirement is that it is clear that the various parties can implement the decision immediately. It may also be subject to careful scrutiny, particularly by a Party who may be dissatisfied with the decision. It is also possible that the *Adjudicator*'s decision is produced in some future arbitration or litigation.

The precise nature of the dispute referred to the *Adjudicator* should be stated. The decision might comprise the *Adjudicator*'s opinion on what, say, the *Project Manager*'s decision should have been in accordance with the contract. It might include assessment of a compensation event, what money is payable by one Party to the other or what changes to the programme are required.

The latter point may cause difficulty, since it is likely that the programme has been revised since the events which gave rise to the dispute took place. For instance, there may have been concurrent delays and subsequent delays. Thus the decision should be the effect of the relevant event upon the Completion Date, assessed at the time of the event. The Parties will then be able to take account of this decision in further revisions of the programme.

Other matters which, for completeness, should be included in the *Adjudicator*'s decision are

- details of the contract,
- details of the appointment of the *Adjudicator*,
- circumstances leading to the reference,
- the procedures followed by the *Adjudicator*,
- information upon which the decision is based.

Where contradictory facts are submitted by the parties, the *Adjudicator* should state his findings. He should summarise the arguments submitted to him, and then state his decision clearly. The *Adjudicator* is also required to state the reasons for his decision. These should show how they led to the decision reached.

Submission of a dispute under this clause does not entitle any Party to cease activities. The *Adjudicator*'s decision is binding and must be implemented. It can only be changed by a subsequent decision of the *tribunal*. However, should the *Adjudicator*'s decision change an action or inaction and the *Project Manager* is of the opinion that his or the *Supervisor*'s original action or inaction remains necessary for the completion of the *works* then, subject to it being limited to a change in the Works Information, he is free to further instruct the *Contractor*. A change in the Works Information under these circumstances is a compensation event as are all such changes.

The adjudication 91

91.1 It is important that the Adjudicator has all the relevant information to enable him to put himself in the position of the Project Manager or Supervisor when the action was taken or not taken as the case may be. Information has therefore to be as full as is appropriate to the dispute. The Party submitting the dispute to the Adjudicator is obliged to include full information about the dispute. The other Party should, as quickly as practicable and no later than four weeks after the submission of the dispute, submit to the *Adjudicator* any information upon which he relies by way of a response. Whilst either Party may amend his submission or issue further information and responses within the four weeks after submission (or longer period as requested by the *Adjudicator* and agreed by the Parties), it is intended that this four week (or other) period is used by the Parties to assist the *Adjudicator* in reaching as rapid a decision as is reasonably possible. Similarly the *Adjudicator* may call for information which has to be provided within the four week or other period.

Information which is submitted after the above period has expired is not admissible in the adjudication. The Parties are not permitted to widen a dispute referred to the *Adjudicator* beyond that notified under Clause 90.1.

In complex disputes and for other valid reasons, the *Adjudicator* may require a period greater than the four weeks stated. For example the *Adjudicator* may require time to visit the Working Areas and may need to consult with other people to help him in arriving at a decision. Consequently, whilst an extension of the period requires the agreement of the Parties it is recommended that any extra time sought by the *Adjudicator* should be allowed as not to do so will usually prolong and add cost to the dispute.

91.2 Where a dispute which affects work which has been subcontracted arises, and which may constitute a dispute between the *Contractor* and a Subcontractor as well as between the *Contractor* and the *Employer*, there is provision for the matter to be resolved between the three parties by the main contract *Adjudicator*. This saves time and expense and prevents a dispute being dealt with by different adjudicators who may make different decisions. This procedure is only possible if the terms of the subcontract permit the *Contractor* to submit the subcontract dispute to the main contract *Adjudicator*.

The *Adjudicator* 92

92.1 The person appointed as the *Adjudicator* is named in the Contract Data.

The relevant experience, qualifications and general ability of any prospective *Adjudicator* must be carefully considered. The qualities of an *Adjudicator* should, as a minimum, include:

- knowledge of the procedures in the ECC,
- a full understanding of the roles of the *Project Manager* and the *Supervisor*,
- a full understanding of how construction costs arise and how they are affected by changes to plan,
- knowledge of construction planning and of how plans are affected by changes,
- the ability to obtain technical assistance when his own technical knowledge does not cover the matter in dispute,
- the ability to obtain up-to-date information about construction costs when he does not have access to relevant cost data,
- an appreciation of construction risks and how allowances for them should be set.

Normally the *Adjudicator* will be appointed jointly by the *Employer* and the *Contractor* under the NEC Adjudicator's Contract, under which the Parties indemnify him against claims, etc. His fees are shared equally between the Parties to the dispute, regardless of his decision.

The *Adjudicator*'s task is stated. He will in his review of the action or inaction decide and state the duties and obligations of the *Project Manager*, *Supervisor* or the Parties which are to be followed and complied with as a contractual obligation. If he decides in the *Contractor*'s favour but it is too late for the action or inaction to be implemented he will deal with the matter by deciding the effect on the Prices and Completion Date using the same assessment procedure that is used for compensation events.

In other circumstances, it may be appropriate for the *Adjudicator* to change the disputed action or inaction. For instance, where the *Contractor* disputes the existence of a Defect which has been notified by the *Supervisor*, the *Adjudicator* may decide in the *Contractor*'s favour.

If so, the *Contractor* would be relieved of any obligation to correct, if corrective work has not started. If the alleged Defect has been 'corrected', the *Adjudicator* would decide on the financial and time effects. However, as in other instances, should the *Project Manager* still require additional or remedial work then he may instruct such work as a change to the Works Information. This would be a normal compensation event.

If the dispute concerned an amount due as certified by the *Project Manager* and the *Adjudicator* decides that the amount certified was incorrect, the *Project Manager* will be required to make a correction in the next certificate and include interest under Clause 51.3.

If the *Adjudicator* disagrees with the *Project Manager*'s assessment of delay to the Completion Date, he will overrule the *Project Manager*'s decision and the Completion Date will be set in accordance with what the *Adjudicator* decides. If, however, it is too late to allow the *Contractor* to revise his programme, the *Adjudicator*'s decision will be in respect of the effect on the Prices only.

This clause requires communications between a Party and the *Adjudicator* also to be communicated to the other Party. The Party making the communication should also issue it to the other Party.

92.2 This clause provides for the appointment of a replacement *Adjudicator* if the *Adjudicator* resigns or is unable to act. One possible reason for an *Adjudicator* not being able to act is if there is a conflict of interest.

The *Employer* should check for conflicts of interest before naming a proposed *Adjudicator* in the Contract Data.

Any existing disputes on which the original *Adjudicator* has not made a decision will be referred to the replacement *Adjudicator* after his appointment. The time periods in the contract will then run from submission of the disputes to the replacement *Adjudicator*.

Review by the *tribunal* 93

93.1 The *Employer* must choose and insert in the Contract Data the *tribunal* which will settle a dispute if either party does not accept the *Adjudicator*'s decision. The choice will normally be either arbitration or the courts. Under no circumstances should an individual be named.

A dispute cannot be referred to the *tribunal* unless it has first been referred to the *Adjudicator*.

Tribunal proceedings cannot start before Completion of the whole of the *works* or termination. In the event of an award at the *tribunal*, interest will accrue under Clause 51.3 and could be significant.

93.2 If the *tribunal* is arbitration, the arbitration procedure is that stated in the Contract Data. Such procedure generally deals with appointment of arbitrators and replacement arbitrators and time limits. A number of countries have their own standard arbitration procedures.

If the chosen arbitration procedure does not provide for the appointment and replacement of the arbitrator, the *Employer* should include the necessary procedures in the Contract Data.

In defining those procedures the following aspects of arbitration should be included.

- On matters of procedure the power of decision should be given to the arbitrator and not the Parties or their legal representatives once appointed.
- The arbitrator should have certain qualifications which should include
  - appropriate training,
  - the ability to manage an arbitration,
  - qualification in the area of the dispute,
  - qualification in the law of arbitration,
  - available time for the arbitration,
  - the ability to take an active role in the process.
- As far as possible, the exchange of written statements, including experts' reports, should apply.
- The arbitrator must ensure that experts know that their primary duty is to the arbitration and not to the Parties.
- A limited timetable should be defined for oral hearings with equal sharing of time between the Parties.
- Case-management conferences at specified stages of the arbitration should be arranged in order to monitor time and expenditure.
- The arbitration needs to take into account any other specific requirements peculiar to the particular project or its expected disputes.

In the United Kingdom, standard arbitration procedures for civil engineering works are

- The Institution of Civil Engineers' Arbitration Procedure (England and Wales) (1983) and
- The Institution of Civil Engineers' Arbitration Procedure (Scotland) (1983).

In the United Kingdom, standard arbitration procedures for building works are:

- The JCT Arbitration Rules - 18 July 1988

Arbitration procedures frequently used both inside and outside the United Kingdom are

- Rules of Conciliation and Arbitration of the International Chamber of Commerce,
- United Nations sponsored UNCITRAL rules and
- The ACP/EEC Conciliation and Arbitration Rules covering contracts funded by the European Development Fund.

Termination 94

94.1 Both the *Employer* and the *Contractor* have rights of termination. The Party wishing to terminate initiates the procedure by notifying the *Project Manager* and giving his reasons for terminating. If satisfied that there are valid contractual grounds for termination, the *Project Manager* issues a termination certificate promptly.

94.2 Only the *Employer* has a right of termination entirely at his discretion, i.e. without one of the reasons listed in R1 to R21. The *Contractor* can terminate only for one of the reasons listed in the Termination Table. Reasons are given identification references for convenience and are fully described in Clause 95. If the *Employer* wishes to terminate for a reason other than those in R1 to R21, he should state this in notifying the *Project Manager* under Clause 94.1.

The procedures to be followed and the amount due to the *Contractor* are generally functions of the reasons for terminating, although some are independent of the reasons.

94.3 The procedures are given in Clause 96.

94.4 Details of the amount due are given in Clause 97 in conjunction with the Termination Table. The *Project Manager* is required to carry out his assessment of the amount due so that he can certify the final payment within thirteen weeks.

Reasons for termination 95

95.1 The terminology of bankruptcy law varies from country to country. The terms used in this clause are those current in English law but the clause allows for their equivalents in other jurisdictions. Termination may follow the bankruptcy, etc. of either the *Contractor* or the *Employer*.

95.2 The four week period of grace is provided so that the *Contractor* has the opportunity to correct the default. Notification should be issued to the *Contractor* and usually copied to the *Employer*. If after four weeks the *Contractor* has not corrected the default, the *Project Manager* would, by implication, need to advise the *Employer* of the position, so that the *Employer* can exercise his right if he wishes. The *Contractor* may have started to make amends but not fully corrected the default after the four week period. In this case, the *Employer* needs to decide whether or not he wishes to proceed to termination.

Reason R11 applies only to a substantial breach of the *Contractor*'s obligations. Minor breaches are insufficient grounds for the serious step of termination, as a matter of policy.

The bond in Option G and the guarantee in Option H are both to be provided within stated times. This clause effectively extends those periods by four weeks. No time limits are given for providing an advanced payment bond under Option J. However, since this bond is provided as security against the advanced payment, delay in providing the bond merely delays the advanced payment to the *Contractor*, which is sufficient sanction.

Subcontracting of work before acceptance by the *Project Manager* (R13) is a breach of Clause 26.2. However, the right to termination only arises when substantial work is subcontracted before acceptance of the Subcontractor.

95.3 Both of these reasons include the word 'substantially' for the reason that minor defaults of this nature would not be sufficient grounds for termination. The right to termination for a breach of a health or safety regulation is in addition to any sanctions under the applicable law.

95.4 Late payment entitles the payee to interest under Clause 51.2. Right to termination, however, only arises if payment is delayed beyond 13 weeks after the date of the certificate and, under R16, the right belongs only to the *Contractor*. This and other listed reasons can be regarded as special cases of R11.

95.5 These measures are usually outside the control of both Parties. This fact is recognised in the respective procedures and the amount due. Any war which breaks out has to be such that it substantially affects the *Contractor*'s work before it gives rights to termination. The place or type of war is not specified. It is possible that a war does not occur in the country where the *works* are located, but in a country where the *Contractor* is manufacturing a large item of plant, thereby substantially affecting his work.

Rights to terminate under the law (R18) may be a result, in some jurisdictions, of force majeure or frustration.

95.6 These reasons apply to instructions which relate to substantial or all work. Again, judgement is needed to interpret what constitutes substantial work. Procedures and payment depend on which Party was responsible for the default which led to the instruction. R21 provides for an instruction which resulted from the default of neither Party.

Procedures on termination 96

96.2 Under procedure P2, the *Employer*'s right to enforce assignment of the benefits of a subcontract will be subject to the terms of the subcontract. In certain cases, a new contract (novation) may be necessary.

Procedure P3 is particularly useful to an *Employer*, where there is substantial falsework or other major temporary works.

Payment on termination 97

97.1 The amounts listed in this clause (A1) are due whatever the reason for termination.

Actual Cost reasonably incurred in expectation of completing the work should include costs which the *Contractor* can show have not been recovered within the normal amount due.

These amounts (A2 to A5) depend on the particular grounds of termination (see Termination Table). Generally, where termination occurs because of the *Contractor*'s default, the *Contractor* is not reimbursed the cost of removing his Equipment. He must also pay the *Employer*'s additional costs for completing the *works*, representing at least some of the damages which the *Employer* suffers arising from the *Contractor*'s breach of contract.

SECONDARY OPTION CLAUSES

Option G: Performance bond

Performance bond G1

G1.1 Where a performance bond is required by the *Employer* the ideal is that it should be provided by the Contract Date. If that is not achieved, a four week limit is provided as a fall-back. Failure to provide the bond within this period entitles the *Project Manager* to notify the default under Clause 95.2. If the *Contractor* does not provide the bond within a further four weeks, the *Employer* is entitled to terminate. The form of the performance bond should be included in the Works Information and the amount of the bond should be stated in part one of the Contract Data. If the *Employer* wishes the *Contractor* to price the bond separately in his tender, an appropriate item should be included in the *activity schedule* or the *bill of quantities* (if any).

Option H: Parent company guarantee

Parent company guarantee H1

H1.1 Where a parent company guarantee is required by the *Employer*, it should be provided by the Contract Date. If that is not achieved, a four week limit is provided as a fall-back. Failure to provide the guarantee within this period entitles the *Project Manager* to notify the default under Clause 95.2. If the *Contractor* does not provide the guarantee within a further four weeks, the *Employer* is entitled to terminate. The form of the guarantee should be included in the Works Information in part one of the Contract Data. If the *Employer* wishes specific provision for the *Contractor* to price the guarantee separately in his tender, an appropriate item should be included in the *activity schedule* or the *bill of quantities* (if any).

Option J: Advanced payment to the *Contractor*

Advanced payment J1

J1.1 The option of making an advanced payment is intended for contracts in which the *Contractor* has to make a heavy investment at the beginning in order, for example, to buy or mobilise major items of Equipment before construction work starts. The start time for repayment of the advanced payment and the repayment amounts are stated in part one of the Contract Data. It is advisable to set these data so that the advance is fully repaid within the first half of the construction period.

To ensure that an advanced payment is not duplicated, instructions to tenderers should make it clear that, when there is an advanced payment, the *activity schedule* or *bill of quantities* should not be priced to produce another advanced payment. For example, there should not be provision for early purchase of Equipment in the *activity schedule* or method related charges in the *bill of quantities* for equipment purchase if an advanced payment is to be made under this option.

In entering the amount of the advanced payment in the Contract Data, it should be made clear whether the amount is inclusive or exclusive of VAT or other sales tax. If such tax is payable on amounts to be certified later by the *Project Manager*, it would also be due on the advanced payments.

J1.2 This clause allows for the provision of a bond, if required by the *Employer*, as security for the advanced payment. The bond should normally be provided by the Contract Date, but if this is not achieved, the advanced payment can be delayed until not later than four weeks after the *Employer* has received the bond. The form of the bond should be included in the Works Information by the *Employer*. If the *Employer* wishes to make specific provision for the *Contractor* to price the bond in his tender, appropriate items should be included in the *activity schedule* or *bill of quantities* (if any).

If the *Employer* is late in making the advanced payment the financial consequences for the *Contractor* may be significant. The normal provision for interest due on late payments (Clause 51.2) could be inappropriate and is therefore replaced by the assessment of the effect of the delay as a compensation event.

J1.3 The Contract Data should include the minimum number of weeks after the Contract Date, after which the first instalment of the repayment of the advanced payment is included in the assessment. If the instalment is an amount, it should be a simple fraction of the amount of the advanced payment.

The advanced payment will normally be made before the first assessment of the amount due by the *Project Manager* (Clause 50.1). Repayment of the advanced payment takes place gradually as part of the certified payments of the amount due. A consequence of this is that the total of the certified payments made to the *Contractor* under the normal assessment procedure will always be less than the total payment (including the advanced payment) made to the *Contractor* when option J is being used. This must always be borne in mind when including payments under the contract in the internal financial statements of the *Employer* and the *Contractor*.

Option K: Multiple currencies (used only with Options A and B)

Multiple currencies

(Provision for multiple currencies in Options C and D is made in Clause 50.6 and in Options E and F in Clause 50.7.)

K1 This option is used when it is intended that payment to the *Contractor* should be made in more than one currency and that the risk of *exchange rate* changes should be carried by the *Employer*. It is based on the procedure used by the World Bank on development funded projects. The effect is that the *Contractor* is protected from the currency *exchange rate* changes which may take place after a fixed date as they affect designated parts of the work.

If an item is to be paid for by the *Employer* in the *currency of the contract* and the *Contractor* chooses to pay for it, or part of it, in another currency, the *Contractor* carries the risk of changes in the *exchange rate*. Payment to the *Contractor* is not affected.

If, however, the total of the Prices at the Contract Date, which will be expressed in the *currency of the contract*, includes items identified as to be paid by the *Employer* to the *Contractor* in another currency, the *Employer* takes the risk of any movement in the *exchange rate* after the date of the published *exchange rates* stated in the Contract Data. This is achieved by listing the items in the Contract Data and fixing the *exchange rate* to be used for each currency relative to the currency of the contract. This ensures that the *Contractor* is paid the amount of the other currency which he has quoted for the item.

Option K with Option N

When Option K is used in a contract which also includes Option N, and if an index used in the formula for price adjustment is local to the Site, published in the country of the Site, and covers materials which are normally imported to that country, the index will take account of currency *exchange rate* variations between the supplying country and the importing country. Any such materials should not also be covered by the multiple currency arrangement in Option K, otherwise a double compensation for *exchange rate* variation will result.

If an index used in the formula is an index published in the country of origin of a commodity it will not reflect changes in currency *exchange rates* between the country of origin and the country to which the commodity is being supplied. It is then appropriate, if Option K is used, to include this commodity in the list of items for payment in a second currency in order to protect the *Contractor* from currency *exchange rate* variations.

K1.1 The *Employer* should state in the Contract Data which items of work are to be paid for in currencies other than the *currency of the contract*, what those currencies are, the maximum amounts payable in each currency, the *exchange rates* to be used in calculating the payments and their date of publication. *Exchange rates* are usually those published some two weeks before the date for submission of tenders.

K1.2 The limits to the amounts payable in each currency should be stated in the Contract Data. Any limit should be set sufficiently high to allow for any additional payments due to compensation events requiring more of any currency than envisaged at the Contract Date. If there is no limit on the amount of the relevant currency, 'no limit' should be entered.

Option L: Sectional Completion

Sectional Completion L1

L1.1 This option should be included when the *Employer* requires parts of the *works* to be completed before the whole of the *works*. The parts are called *sections*, each of which should be identified in the Contract Data part one, with requirements for the work to be done by the *completion date* of each stated in the Works Information.

An example of a contract including *sections* could be

Section 1	*Contractor*'s design necessary to start other design work by the *Employer*.
Section 2	Work necessary to enable work in another contract to start.
Section 3	Completion of a major Plant item for commissioning for the *Employer*'s use ahead of the rest of the *works*.

Completion of the *sections* is followed by Completion of the whole of the *works*. The *sections* do not make up the whole of the *works* but only establish key dates leading up to Completion of the whole of the *works*.

Each *section* has a *completion date*, either stated by the *Employer* or tendered by the *Contractor*. Delay damages and bonus for early Completion can be related to the *section completion dates* by using Options R and Q respectively.

Option M: Limitation of the *Contractor*'s liability for his design to reasonable skill and care

The *Contractor*'s design M1

M1.1 Without this option the *Contractor*'s liability for his design is strict, that is, it must be in accordance with the Works Information. This option reduces his liability for his design to 'reasonable skill and care'. In any dispute, the burden of proof is on the *Contractor* to demonstrate that he used reasonable skill and care, not upon the *Employer* to show that the *Contractor* did not.

Option N: Price adjustment for inflation (used only with Options A, B, C and D)

In the case of Options A, B, C and D, the *Employer* should decide how the risk of inflation is to be allocated. If he decides to accept this risk himself, he should include Option N. Without Option N, the contract is firm price and the *Contractor* carries the risk of inflationary increases in the costs of labour, plant, materials, etc.

For cost reimbursable and management contracts (Options E and F), the *Employer* already carries this risk since payments are of recorded Actual Cost. These are 'current costs' and automatically include for price increases occurring since the contract was signed.

A target contract requires the *Employer* to decide whether to use price adjustment for inflation. Normal practice is to select it. It is applied to the prices in the *bill of quantities* or *activity schedule* so that the total of the Prices can be fairly compared with Actual Cost and Fee for calculating the *Contractor*'s share.

Defined terms N1

N1.1 The source of the published priced indices to be used should be identified in part one of the Contract Data together with the proportions of the total value of the *works* to be linked to the index for each category. Allowance is made for a non-adjustable portion which represents the portion for which the *Contractor* carries the risk of inflation. The total of the proportions should be one.

Also entered in the Contract Data is the base date which should normally be four to six weeks before the latest date for submitting tenders.

One of the effects of the calculation is that the non-adjustable element in the formula affects the amount of payment for price adjustment made for compensation events. For example, if a compensation event is assessed some time before the work is done, the *Contractor* does not recover the non-adjustable element on the increased costs for the period between the assessment and when the work is eventually paid for. This is similar in principle to the effect of the non-adjustable element on originally tendered work, namely that the *Contractor* does not recover the non-adjustable proportion from the time when the tenders were prepared until the work is paid for. The effect is not penal provided the non-adjustable element is kept to a small proportion of the total factor. A maximum of 10% is reasonable.

If a compensation event reduces the amount of work to be done, the effect is opposite and the deduction from the Prices is less than the full amount according to the proportion of the non-adjustable element.

Price Adjustment Factors N2

N2.1 Quite often, provisional index figures are published which are corrected to final figures at a later date. This clause requires recalculation using final figures where these are different from provisional figures.

N2.2 This clause has the effect of freezing the Price Adjustment Factor at the Completion Date for the whole of the *works*, thus requiring the *Contractor* to carry the risk of inflation of the cost of work done after this date.

If there are sectional Completions (Option L), the effect of this clause is that, if earlier *sections* are finished late but before the last Completion Date, the *Contractor* will be paid price adjustment on late work. This is part of the ECC system in order to avoid the difficulties of sub-dividing payments after a *section* has been completed and sub-dividing the calculation as between work contributing to various sectional Completions. This could be a complex and contentious calculation.

In the extreme case of a relatively small amount of work having to be done well after the main body of the work, the main body of the work becomes exposed to inflation payments if late simply because there is a small volume of work to be done later. The ECC has a means of avoiding this problem which should be borne in mind when preparing a contract. This is to exclude the small amount of work from the definition in the Works Information of work which has to be done before Completion. If this is done, inflation adjustment will freeze even though this work will not be completed.

Compensation events N3

N3.1 Under Clause 63.1, compensation events are assessed on the basis of Actual Cost of work already done and forecast Actual Cost for future work. Actual Cost is assessed using the Schedule of Cost Components in conjunction with the Contract Data, where appropriate. The result is that, in the general case, some Actual Cost will be in current terms (money of the day) and some will be in base date terms – where rates for employees and Equipment are stated in the Contract Data. This clause reduces current Actual Cost to base date levels so that changes to the Prices for compensation events (Clause 63.1) are made in base date terms. When assessments of the amount due are made the Price for Work Done to Date will be adjusted for inflation under Clause N4.1 or Clause N4.2.

If Option N is not selected, the contract is fixed price with respect to inflation. However, compensation events are still assessed using Actual Cost which, in the general case, will be a mixture of current costs and base date costs. Tenderers will need to consider the amount of contingency for the inflation rate which they wish to include in the rates for the SCC stated in the Contract Data.

Price adjustment N4

Options A and B

N4.1 'Each amount due' is the total to date and only the changes in the amount due are certified after each assessment date (Clause 51.1). Thus the total of the three bullet points listed in Clause N4.1 represents the total amount in respect of price adjustment up to the date of each assessment.

Example

Assume the increase in the Price for Work Done to Date (PWDD) in the assessment is £5,000 and the Price Adjustment Factor (PAF) is 0.05 (ie 5% inflation since the base date). The calculation for the first bullet point in Clause N4.1 is

£5000 x 0.05 = £250

The sum of £250, plus the total of the sums resulting from the same calculation in previous assessments, plus any correcting amount resulting from the third bullet point, is the amount for price adjustment included in the amount due.

Options C and D

N4.2 Adjustment for inflation for target contracts is necessary only for the calculation of the *Contractor*'s share and not the periodic payment of the amount due. This arises because the Price for Work Done to Date is the Actual Cost plus the Fee. Actual Cost is current cost and automatically includes any inflation occurring since the base date. However, since the *Contractor*'s share is calculated from the difference between the Prices and the Price for Work Done to Date, the two must be compatible in terms of allowance for inflation. The total of the Prices is derived from either an *activity schedule* or a *bill of quantities*, and it is this which must be adjusted for inflation.

The first of the two bullet points in Clause N4.2 determines the inflationary component of the increase in the Price for Work Done to Date since the last assessment.

Example

Assume the increase in the PWDD for the assessment is £5000 and the PAF is 0.05 (i.e. 5% inflation since the base date). The calculation for the first bullet point in Clause N4.2 is

$$\text{PWDD}\left(1-\frac{1}{1+\text{PAF}}\right) = \frac{\text{PWDD}\times\text{PAF}}{1+\text{PAF}}$$

$$\text{i.e.} \qquad \frac{5000\times 0.05}{1.05} = 238.1$$

The sum of £238.1, plus any correcting amount resulting from the second bullet point, is the price adjustment amount for the assessment and is added to the total of the Prices. The result of this calculation at each assessment is added to the total of the Prices to maintain comparability with the final Payment for Work Done to Date.

Option P: Retention (used only with Options A, B, C, D and E)

Retention P1

The purpose of retention is to enable the *Employer* to retain a proportion of the Price for Work Done to Date as security and as an additional motivation for the *Contractor* to complete the *works*. The procedure used in the ECC has no effect on the *Contractor*'s cash flow in the early part of the contract period (see Figure 4).

The retention option should not be used in Management Contracts (Option F) as the *Employer* is adequately protected by the retention in the subcontracts.

P1.1 The *retention free amount* and the *retention percentage* should be entered in part one of the Contract Data. The amount to be retained from the amount due is related to the Price for Work Done to Date only and not to any other sums.

If the *Employer* prefers to use the more conventional method for retention, this can be effected by entering in the Contract Data the required *retention percentage* and 'nil' for the *retention free amount*. A limit for the maximum amount to be retained could then be added if required.

P1.2 Four weeks after the date of issue of the Defects Certificate is an assessment date (Clause 50.1). In this and any later assessment, retention is reduced to zero.

Option Q: Bonus for early Completion

Bonus for early Completion Q1

Q1.1 Where Completion as early as possible would benefit the *Employer*, whether of the *works* or of a *section* of the *works*, the *Employer* can use this option to motivate the *Contractor* to achieve early Completion. The bonus calculated in accordance with this clause will be included in the assessment occurring at Completion, or at the first assessment date after the date when the *Employer* takes over the *works*.

Option R: Delay damages

Delay damages R1

R1.1 Delay damages are the liquidated damages paid by the *Contractor* when he fails to complete the *works* by the Completion Date. It is recommended that this option is included in most contracts. Under English law and some other legal systems, if it is not included, delay damages are 'at large' and the remedy open to the *Employer* is to bring an action for damages for the *Contractor*'s breach of contract. In this event, evidence of the actual damages suffered by the *Employer* is required.

The amount of delay damages should not exceed a genuine pre-estimate of the damage which will be suffered as a result of the *Contractor*'s breach. They are described as delay damages in the NEC ECC as these are not the only liquidated damages. Others are low performance damages (Option S) and interest for delayed payments in core Clause 51.2.

Appropriate entries for delay damages should be made in the Contract Data. They may comprise loss of rent, loss of profit from a manufacturing facility, costs due to delayed start of another contract, or simply interest on the capital invested in the project for the period during which the *Employer* has been deprived of its benefit. The *Employer* is advised to keep a record of the calculation. Damages greater then a genuine pre-estimate constitute a penalty and are not generally enforceable under English law.

If no entry or a 'nil' entry is made in the Contract Data, it is likely that the *Employer* will be unable to recover any damages. It is also emphasised that, if Option R is included, delay damages are obligatory and if the *Employer* does not claim them on time it is possible that he may lose his rights.

If Option R is used in conjunction with Option L for sectional Completion, an estimate of delay damages should be stated in the Contract Data against the Completion Date for each *section*. A separate entry should be included for delay damages for the whole of the *works*.

Since delay damages are amounts to be paid by the *Contractor*, appropriate deductions are made in the first assessment of the amount due occurring after the Completion Date, and in subsequent assessments up to the earlier of Completion and the date on which the *Employer* takes over the *works*.

R1.2 This clause protects the *Contractor* when he has paid delay damages and a later assessment of a compensation event results in a delay to the Completion Date. This could occur when a compensation event arises at a late stage in the work or if an *Adjudicator* or the *tribunal* changes the assessment of a compensation event and the decision is made after delay damages have been paid.

The *Employer* is required to repay any overpayment of delay damages with interest but does not need to wait for an assessment date to be triggered by Clause 50.1. The date of repayment is an assessment date.

Option S: Low performance damages

Low performance damages S1

S1.1 If the *Contractor* produces substandard work (a Defect such as low quality brickwork, reinforced concrete or electrical insulation) the *Employer* can

- insist on the quality specified in the Works Information being achieved,
- recover the cost of having it corrected by other people if the *Contractor* fails to correct the Defect within the *defect correction period* (Clause 45) or
- accept the Defect and also a quotation from the *Contractor* for reduced Prices, an earlier Completion Date, or both, in return for a change to the Works Information (Clause 44).

Where the performance of the *works* in use fails to reach a specified level due to a design or other fault of the *Contractor* and the Defect is not corrected so that it is listed in the Defects Certificate, the *Employer* should be able to recover the damages he suffers in consequence. This option provides for these damages to be recovered as liquidated damages.

The required performance should be specified in the Works Information e.g.

- the output of an electricity generating station,
- a standard of water quality to be produced by a water treatment plant.

A convenient method of calculating damages for low performance is the assessment of a lump sum to compensate for the loss of performance over the lifetime of the asset. The forecast net present value of the lost performance over the forecast life of the asset is an appropriate amount.

The amounts of damages are entered in the Contract Data part one against different ranges of low performance. Certification of performance by the *Supervisor* would follow a specified performance test to be carried out between Completion and the *defects date*. For example, for a specified performance of an electricity generating station in the Works Information of 100 MW, the entries in the Contract Data could be

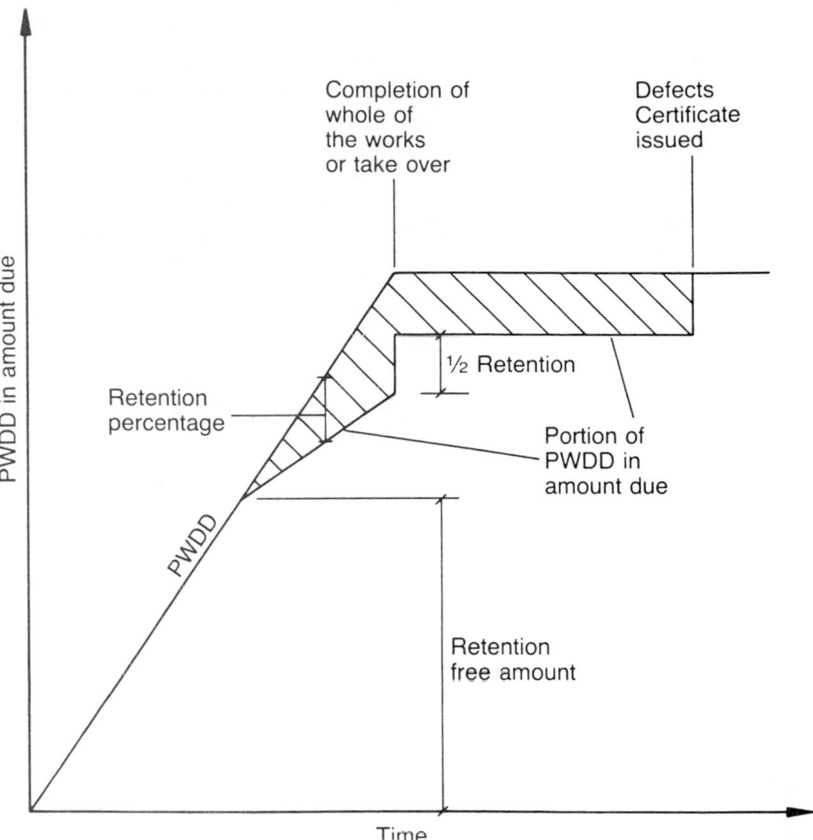

Figure 4. Option P — Retention

- £X000 for performance less than 100 MW but not less than 98 MW
- £Y000 for performance less than 98 MW but not less than 96 MW

continuing down to a 'threshold' performance below which the *works* will be unacceptable to the *Employer* and he would wish to reject them and seek compensation under the general law.

Any deductions of low performance damages is made in the assessment made at the date of issue of the Defects Certificate.

Option T: Changes in the law

Changes in the law T1

T1.1 This clause removes from the *Contractor* the risk of changes in the law which occur after the Contract Date. In certain countries, such changes can have a dramatic effect on the *Contractor*'s costs and on his ability to make progress to complete the *works* on time. Only changes which affect the *Contractor*'s costs are included. Thus changes of law affecting the following are not compensation events:

- income tax or any other tax paid by employees,
- corporation tax or any other charges on profits.

Changes of law affecting the following would be compensation events:

- employment tax paid by the *Contractor*,
- import duties,
- customs payments.

For the purposes of this clause, law would include a national or state statute, Ordinance, decree, regulation (including building or safety regulations) and a by-law of a local or other duly constituted authority or other delegated legislation.

The *Contractor* may notify the *Project Manager* of a compensation event under this option, using the procedure in Clause 61.3. He is most likely to do this when a change in the law has the effect of increasing the cost to him of Providing the Works. However, the clause is reciprocal in the sense that the *Employer* gains the benefit of a change in the law which reduces costs.

Option U: The Construction (Design and Management) Regulations 1994

These regulations apply to the majority of construction work carried out in the United Kingdom. Hence this option should be used wherever the regulations apply. For each project, a planning supervisor and a principal contractor are appointed with extensive powers to manage health, safety and welfare at the design stage, and throughout construction on site.

Regulation 10 requires a health and safety plan which satisfies various requirements, to be prepared before any construction work starts. This plan is initially prepared before the tender stage, and is incorporated in the tender documents. The principal contractor then 'takes over' the plan and develops it to incorporate methods and arrangements to be used by the various contractors and subcontractors on site. Thus it will change throughout the period of construction.

The duties and powers of all parties involved in the project are set out in the regulations and are not repeated in the contract. This optional clause deals with payment arising from application of the regulations. The financial risk is shared between the *Employer* and *Contractor*, the dividing line being based on foreseeability at the time of tender.

Option V : Trust Fund

The ECC Trust Fund is designed to meet one objective. This is the protection of a firm, at any tier in the supply chain, against insolvency of its employer. The protection extends only to covering a payment due for work under his contract which was unpaid at the time of the insolvency.

The Trust Fund's objectives do not extend to protection against late payment. The Engineering and Construction Subcontract already provides significant protection against late payment. It does not contain a 'pay-when-paid' provision and it requires interest to be paid on all late payments.

The Trust Fund is a Secondary Option because of the differences of view amongst clients as to the benefits and the legal differences between different countries. If this Option is chosen, the *Employer* will need to complete a Trust Deed with the *Trustees*. An example of a Trust Deed, compatible with the ECC Trust Fund clause, is included in these notes at Appendix 7.

V1.1 (3) For ease of administration by the *Employer*, the Initial Value of the Trust Fund is set at a level which experience shows corresponds approximately to the maximum payment likely to be made when payments are made at regular monthly intervals.

If Option A has been chosen and only a relatively small number of milestone payments are planned, this clause may need to be amended.

Defined terms V1

V1.1 (4), (5) The definitions of insolvency are identical to those in the Termination Section, Clause 95.1. These definitions may not be appropriate outside the UK.

(6) The list of Beneficiaries is drawn widely to include any firm in the supply chain that is employed to Provide the Works. The phrase 'of whatever tier' means, for example, that the nth subcontractor in the chain is protected against insolvency of the $(n\text{-}1)^{th}$ subcontractor who has employed him to Provide the Works.

The second and fourth bullets of this clause show that the protection of the Trust Fund applies not only to subcontractors of whatever tier, but also to suppliers of whatever tier. However, suppliers to suppliers of the *Contractor* are not specifically mentioned. The example of a Trust Deed (Appendix 7) makes it clear that they are included.

Trust Fund V2

V2.2 The Trust Fund may be established by a cash payment, the provision of a guarantee or by entering into an undertaking with the *Contractor* and the *Trustees*. Public sector clients are likely to use the second or third of these routes. However, if the Fund is established by an undertaking and the *Employer* fails to honour it, enforcement may not be a simple matter. In addition, insolvency of the *Employer* would mean that the undertaking could not be met. For these reasons the option to establish the Fund by an undertaking is only open to public sector employers. Where a bank guarantee is provided or cash payment is made, this risk is avoided, at least with regard to the initial payment.

If government departments or public authorities choose to establish the Fund by an irrevocable undertaking, this will need to be separately drafted. The *Contractor* is a party to the undertaking which helps to confirm the contractual arrangements and means that the *Contractor*, as well as the *Trustees*, could take action against the *Employer* if he did not comply with his undertaking.

Where the Fund is established by a guarantee of the Initial Value the *Trustees* should call down only the amounts which they need to meet Trust Payments. Because of the security arrangements between the *Employer* and the guarantor this is a cheaper option for the *Employer* and it does not hamper the *Trustees.*

V2.3 An appropriate clause has been included for Option V in the ECS which should be used if Option V is chosen in the ECC. That clause makes the Subcontractor aware of the existence of the Trust Fund, of his right to be informed of the terms of the Trust Deed and of his obligation to inform the subsubcontractors and suppliers. The *Employer* will need to provide a copy of the Trust Deed to the *Contractor.*

It is not possible to remove entirely the risk to the *Employer* that he may pay twice for the same work. This could occur when a party in the chain has received a payment by the normal contractual route and becomes insolvent before passing on any money owed to parties down the chain. This is a risk which *Employers* will need to accept if they wish to provide the protection afforded by the Trust Fund.

Trust Deed V3

V3.1 (2) A Beneficiary who receives a payment from the *Trustees* would also be a creditor of the insolvent contractor. If any funds become available from a liquidator or receiver, this clause ensures that the Trust Fund is reimbursed. An assignment of rights by the Beneficiary is preferable to an undertaking, since there is a risk that the latter might not be honoured.

(3) This clause gives considerable discretion to the *Trustees* to decide the amount and timing of a Trust Payment. However, *Trustees* owe a duty to the Beneficiaries and so their right to exercise discretion is not one they can exercise carelessly. Nevertheless, discretion is required as, for example, there may be insufficient money in the Fund to make a full payment immediately. In complicated cases the *Trustees* may need to seek professional advice as to the amount due, but still be left with the need to make their own judgement.

A Beneficiary is an unsecured creditor of the insolvent party. The *Trustees* will need to take account of the funds likely to be available for unsecured creditors rather than for secured creditors who rank ahead of them.

(4) This clause requires the *Employer* to top up the Trust Fund when payments are made out of it, with no limit placed on his obligation to do so. The alternative approach of a fixed sum is not appropriate because, whilst it does limit the exposure of the *Employer*, it could not be guaranteed to provide the required protection throughout the contract period.

(5) Interest accruing on the Trust Fund is returned to the *Employer*. If there are no calls on the Fund, this will offset the cost to the *Employer* of lack of access to the capital tied up in the Fund.

Any amount remaining in the Fund is paid to the *Employer* even if it has been established by guarantee, as the guarantor will have made his own arrangements for security with the *Employer*. The arrangements made for this security will depend on circumstances and these may result in the *Employer* making a separate agreement that any amounts remaining in the Fund are paid to the guarantor.

When the Fund is established by guarantee the amount to be returned would derive from sums recovered from Beneficiaries or from surpluses in payments made to the *Trustees* by the guarantor.

This clause also limits the time period over which Beneficiaries are entitled to submit claims. This is set at the date of issue of the Defects Certificate rather than, say, Completion as a significant amount of work might be done after Completion, especially by specialist subcontractors, on some projects.

Option Z : Additional conditions

This option should be used where the *Employer* wishes to include additional conditions. These should be carefully drafted in the same style as the core and optional clauses, using the same defined terms and other terminology. They should be carefully checked for consistency with the other conditions.

Additional conditions should be used only when absolutely necessary to accommodate special needs such as those peculiar to the country in which the work is to be done. The flexibility of the ECC main and secondary options minimises the need for additional conditions. Additional conditions should never be used to limit how the *Contractor* is to do the work in the contract as this is part of the function of the Works Information.

SCHEDULE OF COST COMPONENTS

GENERAL NOTES

The ECC contains a Schedule of Cost Components (SCC) and a Shorter SCC. This section of General Notes applies to both versions of the SCC. It is followed firstly by notes which are specific to the full SCC and then by notes on the Shorter SCC. The term 'full SCC' is not used in the contract but is used in these notes to distinguish it clearly from the Shorter SCC.

Compilation

Matters which have been considered in compiling the SCC are:

- the treatment of compensation events in terms of their impact on the costs incurred by Subcontractors (see below),
- the ECC definitions of 'Plant and Materials' and 'Equipment' which differ from those found in most traditional contracts,
- the principle that cost components which are not listed in the SCC are to be covered by the Fee, for which the cost components are not separately listed.

Use of the SCC

The SCC has two uses:

- It defines the cost components which are included in an assessment of changed costs arising from a compensation event. This applies to Options A, B, C, D and E.
- It defines the cost components for which the *Contractor* will be directly reimbursed. This applies to Options C, D and E.

The SCC does not apply to Option F (Management contract) where the definition of Actual Cost is restricted to payments due to Subcontractors for work which the Management *Contractor* is required to subcontract.

For Options A and B the SCC is a complete statement of the cost components under the definition of Actual Cost, whether work is subcontracted or not.

For Options C, D and E the Actual Cost includes payments due to Subcontractors in addition to the cost components in the SCC, for work which is not subcontracted.

Working Areas

The Site is defined as the area within the *boundaries of the site* stated in the Contract Data. This area will comprise locations provided by the *Employer* for the *works*. *Contractors* often make use of other areas, sometimes adjacent to the Site, for a variety of purposes such as batching plant, temporary workshops and steel bending yards. On some contracts the *Contractor* may establish depots which are distant from the Site. Where these areas are specific to the contract and closely associated with Site activity, their costs should be included in the SCC rather than covered by the Fee.

In order to achieve this the concept of Working Areas is introduced. The Working Areas include the Site and other areas. It is preferable for the *Contractor* to list in the Contract Data Part two specific areas by location. Sometimes the precise area may not be known at tender or it may be anticipated that the area could change during the contract (for example, where the location of an off-Site batching plant will be moved during the construction of a road or where the *Contractor* is responsible for locating borrowpits). In these cases a generic description of the purpose or type of area should be listed. In addition, further areas may be added to the Working Areas if the *Contractor*'s proposals are accepted under the procedure in Clause 15.1.

Actual Cost: treatment of Subcontractors

The definitions of Actual Cost vary between main options to reflect different treatments of the costs of Subcontractors.

Options A and B

The only use of the SCC is in the assessment of compensation events. Compensation events are assessed as their effect on the *Contractor*'s forecast or recorded Actual Costs. To achieve this satisfactorily the Subcontractors' costs should be available in the same way as the *Contractor*'s costs. All the elements in the SCC apply equally to the *Contractor* and Subcontractors. Thus payments to Subcontractors are not included in Actual Cost. If they were, the effect would be to remove the Subcontractors' costs from an assessment of compensation events. This would also have the effect of absolving the *Contractor* from all payment risks with respect to Subcontractors.

Under Options A and B both the *Contractor* and any Subcontractors are required to show the effects of a compensation event on their forecast costs. The *Contractor* and Subcontractor must prove the effects and this will be easier if they give the *Project Manager* access to their accounts and records.

Options A and B (Clause 63.10) provide for the Fee allowance to be included for the *Contractor* within the assessment of a compensation event but not a doubling up by adding yet a further fee for Subcontractors. The notes on Clause 63.10 explain this reasoning in detail.

Options C and D

In these options, compensation events result in an adjustment of the target and the argument used for Options A and B could be applied to target contracts. However, these are contracts with low risk to the *Contractor* and it is intended that the *Contractor* should be protected from payment risks with respect to Subcontractors. Thus payments to Subcontractors are included in Actual Cost for both the assessment of the compensation events and for the calculation of the Price for Work Done to Date. It follows that the *Employer* pays both the *Contractor*'s Fee and the Subcontractor's Fee.

Option E

Cost reimbursable contracts place a very low level of risk on the *Contractor*. As with target contracts the *Contractor* is intended to be protected from payment risks with respect to Subcontractors and payments to Subcontractors are included in the Actual Cost. The *Employer* pays both the *Contractor*'s Fee and the Subcontractor's Fee.

In these contracts there is no tendered price to adjust for compensation events. However, the compensation event procedure is in core and therefore applies to Option E. This is to ensure that *Employers* receive forecasts of the effects of compensation events for budgeting and planning purposes. It also provides a basis for decisions such as whether to proceed with a proposed change to the Works Information.

Option F

The Management Contractor is intended to be insulated from the cost risk of those subcontracts which he is required to place. This is achieved both in calculating the Price for Work Done to Date and in assessing compensation events by stating that the Actual Cost is only the payments due to Subcontractors. All the Management Contractor's other costs must be allowed for in his Fee. The Fee will therefore need to include not only head office overheads and profit but all direct costs including those of any subcontract he places at his own discretion.

In stating that for Option F, as well as for Options C, D and E, the *Contractor* is protected from payment risks with respect to Subcontractors, it could appear that the *Employer* has no control over risks from Subcontractors. This is not the case as other clauses give the *Project Manager* the right to influence the form of subcontract and the selection of Subcontractors and to disallow payments for compensation events to Subcontractors where these have not been properly assessed in accordance with the terms of the subcontract. When preparing the tender documents for a management contract the *Employer* or his *Project Manager* may wish to include more detailed procedures for the selection and control of Subcontractors. These should be stated in the Works Information.

Where the *Employer* is directly reimbursing Actual Cost he is entitled to

- benefit from all discounts received by the *Contractor*, including any bulk purchase discounts received by head office
- pay prices for subcontracted and supplied goods and services which are fair prices obtained in the open market. For example, the *Employer* is entitled to protection from paying artificial prices for plant-hire or roadstone products supplied by *Contractor*-owned subsidiaries.

Clause 52.1 is intended to achieve these aims.

Disallowed Costs

The inclusion of a cost element in the SCC does not necessarily entitle the *Contractor* to payment of all costs incurred. The definitions of Disallowed Cost in Options C, D and E (Clause 11.2.(30)) and in Option F (Clause 11.2(29)) identify the circumstances in which costs will be excluded from Actual Cost. These clauses are intended to motivate the *Contractor* to work efficiently and to enable him to be reimbursed for all his costs itemised in the SCC if he does. If he does not work efficiently, for example by ordering materials above the level required to cover loss and wastage, the appropriate costs can be disallowed by the *Project Manager*.

The cost components

If the *Employer* believes that any item in the SCC is not relevant he can delete it for a specific contract. However, an item can still be left in the list even if no costs arise in relation to it.

If there are particular costs which the *Contractor* will have to pay which are not covered (which might be the case on some overseas contracts) the *Employer* can add items to the list when preparing the tender documents. Occasionally it may be appropriate to include in the SCC items presently covered in the Fee.

In part two of the Contract Data there are three groups of entries relevant to the SCC. The first group 'Data for SCC' requires the tenderer to provide data which can be used with either the full or Shorter SCC. The next group is used only with the full SCC and the final group is used only with the Shorter SCC.

NOTES ON THE FULL SCC

People 1

11 Three categories of people are identified whose costs can be included as Actual Cost. Items 11, 12 and 13 list the specific cost components which can be included.

The first category of people excludes *Contractor*'s staff who are working, for example, at head office. Their costs must be allowed for within the Fee, as is normal practice on reimbursable contracts.

The second category deals with *Contractor*'s staff and labour who are required to work within the Working Areas for a relatively short period. This may be on work which was unplanned at tender but has arisen due to a compensation event. The minimum one week working period is included to avoid the disputes which can occur over whether the costs of such people are covered by the Fee.

The third category deals with, for example, the appointment of specialist consultants who may be required as the result of a compensation event.

12 If the *Employer* wishes, the full SCC may be amended for a particular contract by replacing items 12(c) and (d) by more specific components. Examples include payments for

- working at height,
- working in exposed conditions,
- trades supplements,
- plus rates,
- shift allowances,
- tool allowances,
- local allowances,
- food allowances and
- company cars.

13 Item 13(j) could also be made specific if required. Examples include payments by the *Contractor* for

- taxes in respect of employees,
- National Insurance contributions,
- payments under employment law,
- levies for industrial training (if required by law) and
- employer's liability insurance.

The full SCC need not be more specific unless it is judged that dispute is likely if a specific item is not defined. If it is judged necessary to define one specific item, then all other items which would fall under items 12(c) and (d) and 13(j) should also be defined.

Equipment 2 Equipment covers *Contractor*'s materials, fuels and other consumables, scaffolding, machinery, testing equipment, transport, construction plant, temporary works, cabins, workshops, etc. However, for simplicity, the full SCC treats some 'Equipment' such as tools, survey instruments, computers, laboratory equipment, cabins and workshops, as an overhead under the 'Charges' section.

The full SCC covers

21 Equipment hired from sources external to the *Contractor* or his parent company,

22(c) Equipment hired by the *Contractor* from a subsidiary or from a member company of the *Contractor*'s parent group,

22(a) Equipment owned by the *Contractor*, i.e. purchased from external sources either new or second hand, or purchased from a subsidiary or a member company of the *Contractor*'s parent group, and

22(b) Equipment purchased by the *Contractor* under a hire purchase or lease agreement. This category is included because the question of 'ownership' is legally complex and treated differently under the laws of different countries. The legal issues of vesting this category of Equipment are also complex and some *Employer*s may wish to preclude the *Contractor* from bringing such Equipment to Working Areas. If so a special condition is required.

For 21 the Actual Cost is the hire cost and includes operators if the item of Equipment is charged by the hirer on an all inclusive basis. If the operators of hired Equipment are shown as a separate charge by hirers then these operators should be costed under the people item as required by item 25 of the SCC.

For 22(c) it is not appropriate for Actual Cost to be the inter-company charge as it is difficult to assess whether internal rates are fair commercial rates. Thus a surrogate 'hire rate' is needed and a 'depreciation charge' approach is adopted.

For Equipment owned, hire purchased or leased by the *Contractor*, the Actual Cost for 22(a) and (b) is also dealt with by a depreciation and maintenance charge, irrespective of its source, using item 22 of the full SCC. This is intended to streamline the process of identifying the costs of *Contractor* - owned Equipment and to ensure a charge rate is readily identifiable when assessing compensation events. The starting point is to calculate the depreciation and maintenance charge which is a cost per week.

Percentage for Equipment depreciation and maintenance

One purpose of this percentage is to avoid disputes over interest on capital used to purchase Equipment, sinking funds for replacement Equipment and inflation effects between purchase and resale. The *Contractor* will cover the risks in the value he tenders for the percentage. The percentage should also allow for any maintenance costs which are not covered by other items in the full SCC.

Restraint is provided as the percentage is quoted in competition. It is recommended that the *Employer* includes for the effect of the percentage in assessing tenders. This is achieved by stating in the instructions to tenderers that a specified amount will have the percentage applied to it and added to the tender value for tender assessment. (See notes on part two of the Contract Data - Tender Assessment.)

Under Options A & B special consideration should be given to Equipment which will be procured, modified or upgraded by the *Contractor* as a 'one-off' specifically for the contract. Unless such consideration is given, an adverse cash flow may result together with an unrepresentative percentage for Equipment depreciation. Similarly a unique or unusual piece of equipment may distort the percentage for depreciation.

For Option A it is recommended that items are included in the *activity schedule*.

For Option B due allowance should be made in *bill of quantities* rates for the financing of Equipment until utilised on the *works*. Alternatively items can be inserted in the Method Related Charges where the *method of measurement* allows.

On reimbursable contracts using the depreciation and maintenance charge method for new Equipment or for Equipment which is procured and modified or upgraded prior to its use in the Working Areas may again result in an adverse cash flow when compared with normal practice. Normal practice would charge the cost of procuring and upgrading to Actual Cost and then credit the Actual Cost with the residual value at the end of contract usage. To offset this it is recommended that the *Employer* provides an advanced payment (Option J) for the procurement, modification or upgrading of the Equipment and, if Option C or D is used, includes separate items, respectively, in the *activity schedule* and *bills of quantities*. Normal practice, as described above, should be used for Equipment procured, upgraded or modified to meet the requirements of, or as a consequence of, a compensation event.

The depreciation and maintenance charge calculation is based on the actual purchase price or first cost paid by the current owner of the item of Equipment within the *Contractor*'s organisation. Under all Options, earlier (i.e. prior to Contract Date) repairs, modifications, major overhauls, rectification and upgrading are to be included in the percentage for Equipment depreciation. This could appear to undervalue an old but effective item of equipment such as a crane barge for off shore work and/or where the item is relatively scarce and expensive, such as a dredger, or where the item has previously been modified or upgraded, such as a concrete train. In such cases, which should be infrequent, the *Contractor* should set the percentage for Equipment depreciation and maintenance at an appropriate level or preferably show both a general percentage for ordinary Equipment with a specific percentage against an intended special item.

Item 22 requires the average working life in weeks to be established. In the absence of any specific information, the table shown below can be used as a guide.

Guide to depreciation rates

Type of Equipment	Depreciation rates % per annum
Air tools including air vibrators	50
Bar benders and cropper	20
Barges and floating equipment including any registration, licensing and marine testing	10
Batching and mixing plants	25
Chilling and ice plants	50
Compressors	20
Cranes	
crawler and equipment	15
lorry mounted or mobile	20
tower	15
Dumpers and rubber tyred excavators — small	25
Electric tools including electric vibrators, welding kits and transformers up to 10 kVA	50
Electric workshop machines, welding plants and transformers greater than 10 kVA	20
Generators	
2.5 to 7 kVA	50
greater than 7 kVA	20
Hoists	
passenger and materials, fork lifts, trailers, pallet and workshop trucks	20
Lighting, air conditioning and ventilation equipment	20
Macadam producing plants	20
Non-mechanical equipment, falsework and scaffolding	10
Paving equipment	
concrete	20
macadam	20
Piling rigs	20
Piling equipment other than rigs	35
Pumping equipment	25
Railway equipment other than for tunnelling	10
Rollers and compactors	20
Tractors, excavators, earthmoving and bulk material handling equipment	20
Tunnel boring machines	33
Tunnelling equipment other than boring machines	20
Vehicles including truckmixers, sweepers and bowsers	
taxed for public highways	25
untaxed for off public highway use	30

NB: All Equipment is generally assumed to be available for 50 weeks per annum except earthworks equipment which is assessed at 30 weeks per annum

The percentage for Equipment depreciation and maintenance must include for the cost of any necessary registration, duties, tests and testing of equipment and the fees and taxes on equipment.

Item 22 of the full SCC requires the time required for Equipment (expressed in weeks or part weeks) to be established. Whole days are to be expressed as two twelfths of a week.

When applying item 22 of the full SCC to the assessment of a quotation for a compensation event the number of weeks or part weeks required will be an estimate of the whole period the Equipment is to be in the Working Areas for and as a consequence of the compensation event. This is regardless of whether the Equipment will be working, temporarily idle or put on standby. In the case of idle or standby time there is to be a deduction from the idle or standby time of the first half day in recognition of a utilisation allowance.

To achieve the most economic solution in the event of Equipment no longer being required or if prolonged standby time is anticipated the *Project Manager* may instruct the Equipment to be removed. In this case compensation is limited at the date of the instruction to the cost of demobilisation. If the Equipment is required to be returned the cost of transport, erection and remobilisation will be payable.

23 Some items of Equipment will be consumed in carrying out the *works*. These include fuels, lubricants, shuttering materials, welding rods and other similar items. For Equipment which is consumed the Actual Cost is the purchase price.

Plant and Materials

3 The definition of Plant and Materials (Clause 11.2(10)) makes it clear that a charge to Actual Cost can only be made for those items which are intended to be included in the *works*.

The Disallowed Cost clause in Options C, D and E (Clause 11.2(30)) is designed to deter the *Contractor* from excessively over-ordering Plant and Materials, and permit the cost of surplus Plant and Materials to be disallowed after allowing for reasonable wastage. This should be taken into account when assessing Actual Cost under items 31(a) and (b). However, item 31(b) does allow payments for removing Plant and Materials from the Working Areas to be included in Actual Cost. An example of the need for this would be when an item of Plant and Materials is not required due to a change in the Works Information.

The Disallowed Cost clause in Options C, D and E and in Option F (Clause 11.2(29)) also permits costs to be disallowed if a procurement procedure stated in the Works Information has not been followed. This could be particularly relevant to the procurement of Plant and Materials.

Charges: Percentage for Working Areas overheads

44 On reimbursable contracts the items listed under item 44 are usually paid as Actual Cost, although in some contracts they have been treated as overheads and covered by a pre-defined percentage. The percentage is usually applied to the Actual Cost of people, i.e. staff and labour. The latter is administratively simpler and places a little more risk on the *Contractor*, including, for example, the risk of excessive wastage of tools. When the full SCC is used in assessing compensation events the effect on the cost of the items under item 44 would have to be forecast as if they were treated as direct costs. The effort required to do this would be totally disproportionate to their value and there would be a high likelihood of dispute. Consequently they remain as Actual Cost but are treated in a pre-defined way which is common to both target and cost reimbursable contracts and compensation events. The *Contractor* inserts the percentage for Working Areas Overheads in part two of the Contract Data when preparing his tender.

Manufacture and fabrication

5 The use of cost reimbursable contracts is not recommended where manufacture or fabrication outside Working Areas forms a major part of a contract. When they have been used in the past, e.g. for defence procurement contracts, they have tended to cause difficulties in the control and identification of Actual Cost.

The SCC is also used for the assessment of compensation events where quotations are based on the effects of the compensation event on Actual Cost. For manufacture or fabrication contracts this creates difficulties which often result in negotiated price changes in the form of lump sums. One of the reasons for the difficulty is that fabrication shop overheads can be several hundred percent of the labour costs.

The use of a percentage for manufacture or fabrication overheads should simplify the administration in both these cases. It is tendered in competition and can be used in assessing tenders in a similar way to the percentage for Equipment depreciation and maintenance.

Item 2 of the full SCC is restricted to Equipment used within Working Areas and therefore equipment, machinery, tools, etc. used in fabrication shops outside the Working Areas must be allowed for in the overheads percentage.

Item 5 excludes the costs of manufacture or fabrication of Plant and Materials which are 'off the shelf'. These are covered by Item 3 of the full SCC.

For Options A and B the SCC is used only to assess compensation events. The definitions of Actual Cost in these options mean that the effects of a compensation event on the costs of manufacture or fabrication done either within or outside the Working Areas are dealt with using the SCC. This applies to both the *Contractor* and his Subcontractors.

For Options C, D and E the definitions of Actual Cost, together with the preamble to the SCC, mean that manufacture or fabrication done by the *Contractor*, either within or outside the Working Areas, is paid for at Actual Cost, using the appropriate part of the SCC. However, for manufacture or fabrication done by Subcontractors in these Options, the SCC does not apply irrespective of where the work is done.

Design 6

Components of design costs need to be included in the SCC so that compensation events which affect design costs result in compensation for the *Contractor*. Item 6 is restricted to design done outside the Working Areas. This could have been omitted from the SCC with the effect that such costs are covered in the Fee. However, this would have been unfair on two counts. Firstly because the ECC envisages that a significant amount of design could be done by the *Contractor*, and secondly because consultants' agreements usually provide compensation to consultants for design charges incurred for reasons outside their control.

The costs of designing Equipment are included. As a result the *Contractor* is reimbursed design costs for compensation events which have a significant impact on the design of temporary works.

The policy adopted for design overheads is similar to that for manufacture or fabrication. Consequently the cost of computer facilities, reprographic facilities, etc. is covered by the percentage for overheads.

Insurance 7

The first of these deductions avoids the *Employer* having to pay for costs which the *Contractor* should have insured against. If the *Contractor* does not insure as required by the contract then such costs are at his own risk. (Also see Clause 85.4).

The second deduction ensures that the *Contractor* does not receive double payment as a result, for example, of insurance which he has voluntarily taken or from insuring for a greater cover than required by the contract.

If the *Employer*'s insurers make payments of other costs incurred by the *Contractor* (because the event is an *Employer*'s risk - see Clause 80.1) then it would be appropriate to allow the *Contractor*'s costs to stand against Actual Cost but the *Employer* will be able to meet those costs from the payments from his insurers.

The Fee

All costs not included in Actual Cost are deemed to be covered by the Fee (Clause 52.1) which should also allow for profit.

The boundary between the SCC and the Fee may not be appropriate for all contracts. However, it has been drawn deliberately in order to be clear. To move the boundary for a particular contract requires a deduction or addition to the SCC. If this is being considered, reference to CIRIA Report 85 is recommended.

The following list gives some examples of cost components not included in the SCC. It is not exhaustive and therefore does not form a schedule of the Fee.

- Head office charges and overheads (unless specified for design, manufacture or fabrication through the overhead percentages).
- Insurance premiums — including, for example, employer's liability insurance for the *Contractor*'s staff and labour.
- Corporation tax.
- Advertising and recruitment costs.
- Sureties and guarantees required for the contract including 'fidelity bonds' required for employees who handle large sums of money which may be the *Employer*'s money, especially on a reimbursable contract.
- Some indirect payments to staff, especially on overseas contracts, for example, school fees. There is no principle involved here, only administrative convenience, recognising that contractors have different policies towards the payment of such items.

The *Contractor*'s profit is also excluded from the SCC and must therefore be allowed for in the Fee.

NOTES ON THE SHORTER SCC

Purpose and use

The Shorter SCC is restricted to the assessment of compensation events and cannot be used to determine the cost components for which the *Contractor* will be directly reimbursed under Options C, D and E. For the assessment of compensation events, it can be used by agreement between the *Project Manager* and the *Contractor*, as provided for in Clause 63.11, which applies to all main options except Option F. Clause 63.11 also allows the *Project Manager* to use the Shorter SCC if he so wishes, when he assesses a compensation event under the circumstances described in Clause 64.1.

The Shorter SCC is intended to provide a faster and administratively simpler method of assessing compensation events. It is likely to be useful where there is a large number of compensation events, for compensation events of low value, and on low value contracts where it might be disproportionately expensive in terms of administration to use the full SCC. In these cases, the precise contribution of some of the components in the longer schedule, to the Actual Cost of a compensation event can be difficult to determine. Use of the Shorter SCC should avoid most of the disputes likely to arise in these cases.

Main Differences from full SCC

The Shorter SCC has been developed from the full SCC and hence most of the notes and principles will also apply to the Shorter SCC. However the Shorter SCC has the following significant differences:

- there are fewer specific cost components for people (item 1),
- the cost of Equipment (item 2) is based on published or agreed rates rather than a depreciation and maintenance charge,
- charges (item 4) are all to be allowed for by a tendered percentage for people overheads, which is applied to the cost of people in item 1.

This percentage covers the costs of the components listed in item 4 of the Shorter SCC. Items 4(b) to 4(e) cover the same components as item 4 of the full SCC but are set out differently to emphasise that they are covered by a percentage rather than being separately identified and costed as is the case with the full SCC.

Items 3 (Plant and Materials), 5 (Manufacture or fabrication), 6 (Design) and 7 (Insurance) are identical to the full SCC.

The calculation of the Fee uses the same *fee percentage* for both methods.

Equipment 2

Some items of Equipment will be consumed in carrying out the *works*. These include fuels, lubricants, shuttering materials, welding rods and other similar items. For Equipment which is consumed the Actual Cost is the purchase price (item 25). However, consumed items which are included in the rates in the published list stated in the Contract Data are covered by item 21. They are therefore not separately added as Actual Cost.

The cost components for Equipment in the Shorter SCC make use of published lists and rates, such as the FCEC Schedule of Dayworks carried out incidental to Contract works, published in the United Kingdom. Items of Equipment likely to be used, but which are not included in a particular published list, can be listed separately in part two of the Contract Data, when the *Contractor* submits his tender.

As the definition of Equipment includes scaffolding, temporary sheet piling etc., tenderers should ensure that rates for these are included in item 22 of the Shorter SCC, if they are likely to represent a significant cost and are not included in the published lists referred to in item 21. A possible alternative is for the tenderer to allow for their costs in the percentage for people overheads, but this would incur some risk. If a compensation event requires such Equipment which was not envisaged at tender, the *Contractor* could reasonably not agree to the use of the Shorter SCC for that event. In these circumstances it would be advisable for the *Project Manager* not to choose the Shorter SCC under Clause 63.11 in order to avoid dispute over the amount of the assessment.

It is not recommended that Equipment which is on prolonged standby is assessed using the Shorter SCC. In such events the full provisions of the Schedule of Cost Components should be used as a more accurate and equitable calculation.

The Equipment rates stated in the published lists will require adjustment by the 'percentage adjustment for listed Equipment' referred to in item 22 and tendered in part two of the Contract Data. This adjustment is required because, for example, the rates in the FCEC Schedule of Dayworks includes an element for overheads and profit. In the ECC, these are included in the Fee. Hence the rates should be adjusted downwards. Also, in some cases the published rates may not be appropriate to local circumstances, and may need adjusting upwards or downwards.

A combination of these and other relevant factors will need to be taken into account to produce the particular percentage adjustment required.

Charges 4

In the Shorter SCC a percentage is applied to the total cost of people items 11, 12 and 13. Such a procedure is adopted to ease the calculation of payroll burden and payments to Others. The percentage for people overheads, therefore, using the Shorter SCC covers the charges as listed. Item 4(e) in the list is covered by a separate percentage for Working Areas overheads in the full SCC. As this is included within the percentage for people overheads in the Shorter SCC the percentage for Working Areas overheads is not used with the Shorter SCC.

Introductory note for Subcontractors from the NEC Users Group

The NEC Engineering and Construction Subcontract (ECS) is new and different. It is written in plain English. Because it follows the principles of the main ECC you have more involvement in the decision-making processes that could affect your business. This subcontract should therefore be more advantageous to you than many of the traditional forms.

These are the key points you should know:

- The NEC's underlying principle is one of goodwill and co-operation by all for the benefit of all. There is a clear division of function and responsibility and good management is encouraged and rewarded. There is an early warning system. The intention is that foresight is applied in collaboration by all parties to identify and resolve problems before they get out of hand.
- Although the ECS is published by the Institution of Civil Engineers it is eminently suitable for building contracts or any new construction work. It is written in clear language and is 'back to back' with the main ECC. The Subcontractor therefore has the same benefits and obligations as the main Contractor. It does not allow the 'large' main Contractor to browbeat the 'small' Subcontractor.
- It is not a 'pay when paid' subcontract. Payments are made regularly and interest can be claimed on any which are late.
- Variations are generally dealt with 'up front' by means of quotations and are intended to include the full cost, including any additional time which may be needed to execute the variation, and the resources to manage and plan it. You may need additional planning and pricing resources to deal with variations and your main Contractor will generally be willing and able to assist you with this.
- You should find that your cash flow will improve and Final Account agreement will be reached sooner.
- There is a simple dispute resolution system.

Engineering and Construction Subcontract

For this section of the Guidance Notes the word Subcontractor is printed in italics if it is used in reference to the NEC Engineering and Construction Subcontract (ECS). The ECS is based on the ECC in order to achieve identical working for similar contract situations. The reason for this is that the relationship between the *Contractor* and the *Subcontractor* is similar to that between the *Employer* and *Contractor*. There are, however, certain additions and amendments required in the subcontract which arise from the main contract.

The ECC includes (amongst others) the following parties:

- the *Employer*
- the *Project Manager* and
- the *Supervisor*.

The ECS equivalents have been combined into one (the *Contractor)* as it was considered that, while different people in the *Contractor*'s organisation may perform the separate functions, it would be too complicated to have different legal persons for each separate subcontract. This has required some amendments where the ECC text describes actions by the *Employer*, *Project Manager* and *Supervisor*.

All the ECC options have been retained for the subcontract except Option F. Thus, for example, the main contract may be a priced contract with a bill of quantities, and the subcontract may be based on an activity schedule, or on a cost reimbursement option.

To avoid confusion, the following items have been prefixed 'subcontract':

- *works*,
- *starting date*,
- Completion Date and
- Works Information

Other changes are

- Subsubcontractor for Subcontractor,
- Subcontract Data for Contract Data,
- ECC is referred to as the main contract.

The main additions and amendments arising from provisions of the main contract are described below.

Subcontract documents

In preparing the subcontract the *Contractor* must be precise in detailing the documentation which comprises both the Subcontract Works Information and the subcontract Site Information. It is not sufficient for the *Contractor* to merely generalise by, for example, stating 'The Main Contract Works Information and Site Information shall be incorporated into this subcontract'. A properly drafted subcontract must state what these documents are especially if the *Contractor* decides upon a different main Option for the subcontract to that under the main contract.

It is recommended that the *Contractor* chooses a main Option for the subcontract consistent with that of the main contract. However, in some circumstances, the *Contractor* will engage a subcontractor under a different main Option: for example, where the *Subcontractor* is offering a lump sum price (Option A) but the *Contractor* is under an Option B contract.

It is usual for the Subcontract Works Information to be based upon and comprise documentation such as specification and drawings. Similarly subcontract Site Information will most probably be that from the main contract but might be added to by the *Contractor* if, for example, he has carried out further site investigation work prior to seeking to sublet a part of the *works*.

Hence where the *Contractor* is incorporating main contract data into a subcontract precise schedules should be prepared and expressly identified in the Subcontract Data part one.

It may be desirable for the *Subcontractor* to have a knowledge of the full general main contract documentation so that he has notice of them. In this case the *Subcontractor* should be given a copy or, as is more usual, he may inspect them and extract copies of any relevant parts. Either way it is recommended that the general main contract documentation or the relevant parts of it is incorporated in the subcontract by reference in the Subcontract Data.

Because of the inevitable difference in obligations between the main contract and subcontract there are some special considerations which the parties to the subcontract should be aware of.

Disputes

A provision has been included to cater for a dispute arising under the main contract which concerns the subcontract *works*. This enables the *Contractor* to require that such a dispute can be dealt with jointly with the dispute under the main contract by the main contract *Adjudicator*. This avoids two different adjudicators making different decisions on the same dispute.

The subcontract *Adjudicator* may be a person different from the main contract *Adjudicator*. His function is to deal with disputes which arise only between the *Contractor* and *Subcontractor* and which do not concern the *Employer*.

If any of the three parties to a joint dispute disagrees with the *Adjudicator*'s decision, he may refer it to the *tribunal*, as in the case of a dispute between only two contracting parties.

Termination

If the main contract is terminated, the *Contractor* will wish to terminate the subcontracts. The payment consequences depend upon whether the termination is due to the *Subcontractor*'s default or not.

Time periods

Time periods stated in the ECS have been adjusted to allow for associated actions under the main contract. Time limits in the subcontract for sending information to the *Contractor* are less than the times stated in the main contract for sending information to the *Project Manager* in order to allow time for the *Contractor* to incorporate or process the information. Time limits in the subcontract for transmitting decisions or payments to the *Subcontractor* are greater than the equivalent times stated in the main contract, for similar reasons.

Some time periods are not stated in the ECS but, like the main contract, are to be inserted in the Subcontract Data. Examples are a reply to a communication or the submission of a revised programme.

The *Contractor* must ensure that the time periods in the Subcontract Data are adequate for proper reply but not excessive so as to prevent the *Contractor* from sending a similar reply under the main contract.

Design Defects

It may be that, as part of his *subcontract works*, the *Subcontractor* is carrying all of the *Contractor*'s design obligation or possibly only a small portion of it. Whatever obligation is passed to the *Subcontractor* should be reflected in the limit of the *Subcontractor*'s liability for design Defects entered in part one of the Subcontract Data.

Risks and insurance

The *Employer*'s risks remain, and the *Contractor* passes those of his risks under the main contract to the *Subcontractor*, where they apply to the *subcontract works*. Double insurance is largely avoided since the insurance premiums payable by the *Contractor* under the main contract will reflect the proportion of the *works* which are subcontracted.

Under the ECS the risks carried by the *Contractor* for the works subcontracted are passed to the *Subcontractor* for the period from the *subcontract starting date* until the subcontract Defects Certificate has been issued. Outside of this period, with the exception of continuing liabilities, the *Contractor* or *Employer* (depending upon other main contract criteria) carries the risk for the *subcontract works*. Thus if the *subcontract completion date* and *defects date* are earlier than those of the main contract then the *Contractor* must recognise two important factors.

- The *Contractor* will carry the risk of and should ensure that his insurance cover is continuing for the *subcontract works*.
- The *Contractor* will carry the risk of Defects in the *subcontract works* from the conclusion of the *Subcontractor*'s liability for correcting his Defects upon the issue of the subcontract Defects Certificate.

Should it be important, for example, that the *Subcontractor* continues to correct Defects right up to Completion of the whole of the *works* (or even to the issue of the main contract Defects Certificate) then the Subcontract Data part one must properly reflect and include this intention of the Parties by incorporating appropriate *subcontract completion* and *defects dates*.

Notwithstanding the subcontract insurance provisions the *Contractor* still carries responsibility for the performance of the *Subcontractor* in the ECC and the *Subcontractor* is always responsible for insuring his own Equipment and his employees.

Delay damages

When considering delay damages under Options L and R it is not sufficient for the *Contractor* to insert in the Subcontract Data optional statements general wording such as 'delay damages as main contract'. The damages must be a genuine pre-estimate at the time when the subcontract is made of the likely losses that the *Contractor* will suffer if there is a delay by the *Subcontractor*.

If the *subcontract works* are critical or the *subcontract completion date* is coincidental with that of the main contract then it may be that the delay damages under the subcontract will be as those for the main contract. In other circumstances where the subcontract is not critical or concerns only minor works the delay damages must reflect this on the basis of a genuine pre-estimate of the loss the *Contractor* would suffer.

Guidance notes

Detailed guidance notes for the ECS have not been prepared, since the principles can be understood from the ECC guidance notes.

Flow charts

Flow charts for the subcontract have not been prepared, since the logic of the procedures can be understood from the ECC flow charts.

APPENDIX 1

Clause numbering system

1 General

Core			Options			
Cl. no.	**Title**	**Para. no.**	**Cl. no.**	**Title**	**Para. no.**	**Applicable options**
10	General	10.1				
11	Identified and defined terms	11.1 11.2(1) to (17)				
				Prices	11.2(19)	E,F
				Prices	11.2(20)	A,C
				Prices	11.2(21)	B,D
				PWDD	11.2(22)	F
				PWDD	11.2(23)	C,D,E
				PWDD	11.2(24)	A
				PWDD	11.2(25)	B
				Actual Cost	11.2(26)	F
				Actual Cost	11.2(27)	C,D,E
				Actual Cost	11.2(28)	A,B
				Disallowed Cost	11.2(29)	F
				Disallowed Cost	11.2(30)	C,D,E
12	Interpretation and the law	12.1 12.2				
13	Communications	13.1 to 13.8				
14	The *Project Manager* and the *Supervisor*	14.1 to 14.4				
15	Adding to the *working areas*	15.1				
16	Early warning	16.1 to 16.4				
17	Ambiguities and inconsistencies	17.1				
18	Health and Safety	18.1				
19	Illegal and impossible requirements	19.1				

2 The *Contractor*'s main responsibilities

Core			Options			
Cl. no.	**Title**	**Para. no.**	**Cl. no.**	**Title**	**Para. no.**	**Applicable options**
20	Providing the Works	20.1				
					20.2	F
					20.3	C, D, E, F
					20.4	C, D, E, F
21	The *Contrator*'s design	21.1 to 21.5				
22	Using the *Contractor*'s design	22.1				
23	Design of Equipment	23.1				
24	People	24.1 24.2				
25	Co-operation	25.1				
26	Subcontracting	26.1 to 26.3			26.4	C, D, E, F
27	Approval from Others	27.1				
28	Access to the work	28.1				
29	Instructions	29.1				

3 Time

Core			Options			
Cl. no.	**Title**	**Para. no.**	**Cl. no.**	**Title**	**Para. no.**	**Applicable options**
30	Starting and Completion	30.1 30.2				
31	The programme	31.1 to 31.3			31.4	A, C
32	Revising the programme	32.1 32.2				
33	Possession of the Site	33.1 33.2				
34	Instructions to stop or not to start work	34.1				
35	Take over	35.1 to 35.4				
36	Acceleration	36.1 36.2				
					36.3	A, B, C, D
					36.4	E, F
					36.5	C, D, E, F

4 Testing and Defects

Core			Options			
Cl. no.	**Title**	**Para. no.**	**Cl. no.**	**Title**	**Para. no.**	**Applicable options**
40	Tests and inspections	40.1 to 40.6				
41	Testing and inspection before delivery	41.1				
42	Searching and notifying Defects	42.1 42.2				
43	Correcting Defects	43.1 to 43.3				
44	Accepting Defects	44.1 44.2				
45	Uncorrected Defects	45.1				

5 Payment

Core			Options			
Cl. no.	**Title**	**Para. no.**	**Cl. no.**	**Title**	**Para. no.**	**Applicable options**
50	Assessing the amount due	50.1 to 50.5			50.6 50.7	C, D E, F
51	Payment	51.1 to 51.5				
52	Actual Cost	52.1			52.2 52.3	C, D, E, F C, D, E, F
			53	The *Contractor*'s share	53.1 to 53.5	C, D
			54	The *activity schedule*	54.1 to 54.3	A, C
			55	The *bill of quantities*	55.1	B, D

6 Compensation events

Core			Options			
Cl. no.	**Title**	**Para. no.**	**Cl. no.**	**Title**	**Para. no.**	**Applicable options**
60	Compensation events	60.1(1) to (18) 60.2 60.3				
					60.4 60.5 60.6	B, D B, D B, D
61	Notifying compensation events	61.1 to 61.7				
62	Quotations for compensation events	62.1 to 62.5				
63	Assessing compensation events	63.1 to 63.7				
					63.8 63.9 63.10 63.11	A, C B, D A, B A, B, C, D, E
64	The *Project Manager*'s assessments	64.1 to 64.3				
65	Implementing compensation events	65.1 65.2				
					65.3 65.4 65.5	E, F A, B, C, D E, F

7 Title

Core			Options			
Cl. no.	**Title**	**Para. no.**	**Cl. no.**	**Title**	**Para. no.**	**Applicable options**
70	The *Employer*'s title to Equipment, Plant and Materials	70.1 70.2				
71	Marking Equipment, Plant and Materials outside the Working Areas	71.1				
72	Removing Equipment	72.1				
73	Objects and materials within the Site	73.1 73.2				

8 Risks and insurance

Core			Options			
Cl. no.	Title	Para. no.	Cl. no.	Title	Para. no.	Applicable options
80	*Employer*'s risks	80.1				
81	The *Contractor*'s risks	81.1				
82	Repairs	82.1				
83	Indemnity	83.1 83.2				
84	Insurance cover	84.1 84.2				
85	Insurance policies	85.1 to 85.4				
86	If the *Contractor* does not insure	86.1				
87	Insurance by the *Employer*	87.1 to 87.3				

9 Disputes and termination

Core			Options			
Cl. no.	Title	Para. no.	Cl. no.	Title	Para. no.	Applicable options
90	Settlement of disputes	90.1 90.2				
91	The adjudication	91.1 91.2				
92	The *Adjudicator*	92.1 92.2				
93	Review by the *tribunal*	93.1 93.2				
94	Termination	94.1 to 94.5				
95	Reasons for termination	95.1 to 95.6				
96	Procedures on termination	96.1 96.2				
97	Payment on termination	97.1 97.2			97.3 97.4	A C, D

Secondary option clauses

	Secondary option	Cl no.	Title	Para. no.	Can be used with these main options
G	Performance bond	G1	Performance bond	G1.1	A to F
H	Parent company guarantee	H1	Parent company guarantee	H1.1	A to F
J	Advanced payment to the *Contractor*	J1	Advanced payment	J1.1 to J1.3	A to F
K	Multiple currencies	K1	Multiple currencies	K1.1 K1.2	A, B A, B
L	Sectional Completion	L1	Sectional Completion	L1.1	A to F
M	Limitation of the *Contractor*'s liability for his design to reasonable skill and care	M1	The *Contractor*'s design	M1.1	A to F
N	Price adjustment for inflation	N1	Defined terms	N1.1	A, B, C, D
		N2	Price Adjustment Factors	N2.1 N2.2	A, B, C, D
		N3	Compensation events	N3.1	A, B, C, D
		N4	Price adjustment	N4.1 N4.2	A, B, C, D
P	Retention	P1	Retention	P1.1 P1.2	A, B, C, D, E
Q	Bonus for early Completion	Q1	Bonus for early Completion	Q1.1	A to F
R	Delay damages	R1	Delay damages	R1.1 R1.2	A to F
S	Low performance damages	S1	Low performance damages	S1.1	A to F
T	Changes in the law	T1	Changes in the law	T1.1	A to F
U	The Construction (Design and Management) Regulations 1994	U1	The CDM Regulations 1994	U1.1	A to F
V	Trust Fund	V1 V2	Defined Terms Trust Fund	V1.1 V2.1 to V2.3	A to F A to F
		V3	Trust Deed	V3.1	A to F
Z	Additional conditions of contract	Z1	Additional conditions of contract	Z1.1	A to F

APPENDIX 2

Sample form of tender

The *works* . . . .

TENDER

To:. . . . . (the *Employer*)

Address: . . . .

. . . .

. . . .

. . . .

We offer to Provide the Works in accordance with the Contract Data part one and the attached Contract Data Part two for a sum to be determined in accordance with the conditions of contract.

You may accept this offer on or before [date of last day for acceptance]

Yours faithfully,

Signed: . . . .

Name: . . . .

Position: . . . .

On behalf of: . . . . (the *Contractor*)

Address: . . . .

. . . .

. . . .

. . . .

Date: . . . .

APPENDIX 3

Sample form of agreement

This agreement is made on the . . . . day of . . . . 19. . . . .

- . . . .

  of . . . .

  . . . . (the *Employer*) and

- . . . .

  of . . . .

  . . . . (the *Contractor*)

WHEREAS the Employer wishes to have provided the following works . . . .

NOW IT IS AGREED THAT

1. The Contractor will provide the works in accordance with the conditions of contract
2. The Employer will pay the Contractor the amount due in accordance with the conditions of contract
3. The documents forming part of this agreement are:

   - the Contractor's tender
   - the Employer's letter of acceptance
   - the Contract Data part one
   - the Contract Data part two
   - the following documents

   . . . .

   . . . .

   . . . .

   . . . .

   . . . .

EXECUTED AS A DEED BY THE EMPLOYER

*... (the *Employer*)

by affixing his common seal in the presence of

or * by (name of Director)

.... (signature of Director)

and .... (name of Director or Company Secretary)

.... (signature of Director or Company Secretary)

AND AS A DEED BY THE CONTRACTOR

*... (the *Contractor*)

by affixing his common seal in the presence of

or * by (name of Director)

.... (signature of Director)

and .... (name of Director or Company Secretary)

.... (signature of Director of Company Secretary)

---

* Delete as appropriate

APPENDIX 4

Model tender assessment sheet (to be used only for Options A and B)

This sheet is only for the purpose of assisting the *Employer* to assess tenders and will not be part of the contract. The amounts stated may not be expended and may be exceeded. Other factors may be taken into account in assessing tenders. These may include cashflow effects, advance payments, design by the *Contractor*.

	Item	Amount £
	1. Completion date	
	i.e. x weeks after starting date	
	(x-y) weeks at £ . . . . per week	. . . .
Data for Schedule of Cost Components	2. Equipment Depreciation and Maintenance	
	. . . . % of £	. . . .
	3. Working Areas Overheads	
	. . . . % of £	. . . .
	4. Manufacture and Fabrication	
	Total number of hours . . . . to be divided equally between each of the tendered categories:	
	. . . . . hours at £ . . . . per hour:	
	. . . . . hours at £ . . . . per hour:	
	. . . . . hours at £ . . . . per hour:	
	. . . . . hours at £ . . . . per hour:	
	Sub Total __________	. . . .
	Manufacture and fabrication overheads	
	. . . . . % of £ . . . . (above Sub Total)	. . . .
	5. Design	
	Total number of hours . . . . to be divided according to the number of tendered categories	
	. . . . . hours at £ . . . . per hour:	
	. . . . . hours at £ . . . . per hour:	
	. . . . . hours at £ . . . . per hour:	
	. . . . . hours at £ . . . . per hour:	
	Sub Total__________	. . . .
	Design overheads	
	. . . . . % of £ . . . . (above Sub Total)	. . . .

[Note: The total number of hours will be divided in the following proportions according to the number of categories of employees engaged on design work entered in Contract Data part two. The proportions are stated beginning with the most senior categories.]

2 categories 30% 70%

3 categories 20% 35% 45%

4 categories1 5% 20% 30% 35%

5 categories 10% 15% 20% 25% 30%]

6. People overheads

. . . . . % of £ . . . .

7. Adjustment for Equipment in published list

. . . . . % of £ . . . .

Fee percentage   8. Fee . . . . . % of £ . . . .

9. Tendered total of the Prices   . . . .

TOTAL FOR TENDER
ASSESSMENT PURPOSES ONLY   £ . . . .

NOTES ON PREPARING TENDER ASSESSMENT SHEET

Item 1 This item is included when the Completion Date is tendered.

- The *Employer* decides the value of 'y' and the rate per week
- 'x' is calculated from the Completion Date in Contract Data part two

'y' should be the minimum period which the *Employer* considers possible for providing the works. The amount entered for the rate per week should reflect the value to the *Employer* of early Completion. In many cases, it will be the same as the rate of delay damages for the whole of the works, or the bonus for Completion of the whole of the works, expressed as a weekly rate.

Item 2

- The *Employer* decides the amount
- The percentage is obtained from Contract Data part two

The amount entered by the *Employer* will be based on an estimate of the depreciation and maintenance of Equipment (other than hired Equipment and Equipment used outside the Working Areas) to be used in the assessment of compensation events. This amount will be divided between the two types of cost component data in the main and shorter schedules. The estimate, which can only be approximate, will depend on recorded data available for the type of work to be carried out.

Example From recorded data, typical final cost is say 30% greater than the tendered total of the prices. Equipment content of this is say 25%. Equipment which is not hired and limited to Working Areas is say 15%. Of this, assume 10% will be used in the shorter schedule, leaving 5% for use with the main schedule. Hence the amount to be entered is:-

Employer's estimate of tendered total of Prices x 30% x 5%
= estimated tendered total of Prices x 1.5%.

Item 3

- The *Employer* decides the amount
- The percentage is obtained from Contract Data part two.

The amount entered by the *Employer* will be based on an estimate of the Actual Cost of people, to be used in the assessment of compensation events.

Example From recorded data, typical final cost for a particular type of work is, say 30% greater than the tendered total of the Prices. The 'People content' of this is say 30%. Of this assume 20% will be used in the shorter schedule, leaving 10% for use with the main schedule. Hence the amount to be entered is:-

The *Employer*'s estimate of tendered total of Prices x 30% x 10%
= estimated tendered total of Prices x 3%.

Item 4

- The *Employer* decides the total number of hours
- The rates per hour for each category and the percentage are obtained from Contract Data part two. The number of hours for each category is calculated by dividing the total hours by the number of categories. The amount to which the percentage is applied is the Sub Total calculated from the hours and rates for each category.

The number of categories of employee is tendered by the tenderer and is therefore not known to the *Employer* when preparing tender documents. Since the various categories are not known, it is impossible to divide an estimated total number of hours in a realistic way. Hence for tender assessment purposes, it is suggested that the total is divided equally between the categories. The total hours entered will be based on an estimate of the manufacture or fabrication work to be done in respect of compensation events. This will depend on the amount of such work already in the Works Information at tender.

Example Assume 8,000 hours for manufacture or fabrication work in the main works at tender. Allow total hours for compensation events 8,000 x 30% = 2,400 hours. If the tenderer has entered rates for 4 categories, then 600 hours are entered for each category.

Item 5

- The *Employer* decides the total number of hours.
- The rates per hour for each category and the percentage for design overheads are obtained from Contract Data part two. The number of hours for each category is calculated by dividing the total hours into the proportions stated on the tender assessment sheet. These proportions vary according to the number of different categories of employee entered in Contract Data part two. The amount to which the percentage is applied is the Sub-Total calculated from the hours and rates for each category.

The number of categories of employee engaged on design work is entered in Contract Data part two by the tenderer and is therefore not known to the *Employer* when preparing tender documents. The allocation of hours to each category should then be 'weighted', since a smaller number of hours would be appropriate for the more senior personnel. 'Weighting' should be carried out by the *Employer* in accordance with the proportions stated on the tender assessment sheet. The total hours entered by the *Employer* will be based on an estimate of the design hours required for both permanent and temporary works in respect of compensation events.

Example Assume 20,000 hours of *Contractor*'s design work in main works at tender. Assume 30% of this for compensation events, i.e. 30% of 20,000 = 6,000 hours. If the tenderer has entered rates and descriptions for four categories of employee, the number of hours for each category (in descending order of seniority) will be 900, 1200, 1800 and 2100.

Item 6

- The *Employer* decides the amount
- The percentage is obtained from Contract Data part two

The amount will be based on an estimate of the cost of people in relation to compensation events using the shorter schedule.

Example Assume that the typical final cost is 30% greater than the tendered total of the Prices. 'People content' of this is say 30% and assume only 20% will be used in the shorter schedule.

Amount to be entered is:-

Employer's estimate of tendered total of Prices x 30% x 20%
= estimated tendered total of Prices x 6%

Item 7

- The *Employer* decides the amount
- The percentage is obtained from Contract Data part two

The amount entered by the *Employer* will be based on an estimate of the Actual Cost of Equipment in the published list to be used in relation to compensation events.

Example From recorded data, typical final cost is, say, 30% greater than the tendered total of the Prices. The 'listed Equipment' content of this is say 25% of which say 20% is to be used within the Working Areas, but only 15% used in shorter schedule assessments.

Amount to be entered is:-

Employer's estimate of tendered total of Prices x 30% x 15%
= estimated tendered total of Prices x 4.5%

The rates for Equipment not on the stated published list, and separately listed in the Contract Data part two, cannot be included in the tender assessment, since details are unknown, when the tender assessment sheet is prepared. Hence, these rates must be separately assessed to check that they are in accordance with the general level of pricing of the rates tendered for Equipment in the published list. Any major anomalies should be discussed with the tenderer.

Item 8

- The *Employer* decides the amount
- The percentage is obtained from Contract Data part two

The amount entered by the *Employer* will be based on an estimate of the Actual Cost to be used in relation to compensation events. This will not be the same as the sum of the amounts entered in Items 2 to 7 above, since a number of components of Actual Cost (eg Plant and Materials and Equipment Hire) do not need to be included in the Tender Assessment Sheet.

Example From recorded data, typical final cost for a particular type of work is, say, 30% greater than the tendered total of the Prices.

Amount to be entered is:-

estimated tendered total of Prices x 30%

Item 9

- Tendered total of Prices is the total of the activity schedule (Option A) or the bill of quantities (Option B).

The total for tender assessment purposes is an arbitrary figure and does not represent an estimate of final cost to the *Employer*. It is purely a means of making a fair assessment of tenders, such that tenderers will not be tempted to 'load' certain tendered figures in Contract Data part two.

APPENDIX 5

Contract Data — worked example

Introduction

The following pages show the Contract Data completed for a fictitious contract. The purpose of this example is to help those unfamiliar with the NEC system to complete the tender documents. It should be read in conjunction with the notes included under the chapter 'Tender documents'.

The following points should be noted:

- The ECC text of the Contract Data formats is reproduced as printed, together with the explanatory sentences which are in bold type. The explanatory sentences (e.g. 'Statements given in all contracts' and sentences beginning 'If...') are only for the guidance of users and should not be reproduced on an actual Contract Data.
- For clarity quantities have been inserted in the appropriate places. **The figures given are imaginary and should not be taken as typical and certainly do not have the status of 'recommended by the NEC Panel'.** The examples of entries are not necessarily consistent throughout.
- All the optional statements have been completed so that users can see what should be written if that option is chosen. **In a real enquiry only those statements relevant to the options chosen should be completed.**
- If an optional statement is required it should be inserted in an appropriate position in the actual Contract Data, within the statements for the relevant section of the ECC.
- **The statements in the boxes only provide a very abbreviated commentary on completing the Contract Data and should not be relied on.** Reference must be made to the conditions themselves and to the relevant Guidance Notes for a fuller treatment of topics.
- ***Employers* must decide actual details based on the nature of the contract and the allocation of risk required.**
- **Those drawing up tender documents are advised to take care when completing the Contract Data that excessive risks are not passed to the *Contractor*.** The ECC system is much more flexible than any other published contract and allows a wide range of *Employers* choice of allocation of risks on the *Contractor* which would be limited in other documents. **Common sense needs to be applied otherwise bids will reflect the unrealistic aspirations of the *Employer*.** In particular combinations including tight programmes, extended defects dates, large bonds, fixed prices, large retentions and heavy damages should only be used if the *Employers* key strategy demands them.
- **The words of the ECC Contract Data formats should be reproduced without change.** Users of the ECC are granted a limited licence by the Institution of Civil Engineers to reproduce the text in tenders solely for the purpose of inviting, assessing and managing contracts.

Part one — Data Provided by the *Employer*

Statements given in all contracts

1. General

- The *conditions of contract* are the core clauses and the clauses for Options **A,G,H,P,R,S,U and Z** of the second edition (1995) of the ECC Engineering and Construction Contract.

Choose a Main Option (A to F) and the Secondary Options appropriate to the contract. Make sure Secondary Options are compatible with the Main Option chosen.
GN on "Contract Strategy"

- The *works* are
the design, supply, installation and commissioning of an Automatic Unloading System for Road Borne Dry Feed.

Describe the *works* clearly but briefly. T description should enable the *works* to be identified but need not go into the detail which will be set out in the Work Information. It may be helpful to includ the location of the *works* if this is not otherwise clear, in this example by the addition of 'at Spearshead Works, Bristo

It is suggested that a briefer title be use on general correspondence together wi the *Employer's* reference number etc. T only other place where the full description need be used is on the Form of Tender.

- The *Employer* is

Name **European Grain plc**

Address **Long Acre Industrial Estate**
Spearshead
Bristol
BS8 2LR

The *Employer's* legal name and usual address are given here. The address need not be the registered office unless required by local or applicable law.

- The *Project Manager* is

Name **Mr F Giles**

Address **Long Acre Industrial Estate**
Spearshead
Bristol
BS8 2LR

It is essential that the person chosen as *Project Manager* must be sufficiently close to the work and have the time to carry out his duties effectively. The ECC assumes the *Project Manager* has the *Employer's* authority to carry out the various actions and make the various decisions which are required.
GN on "Project Manager"

The address should be the normal location of the *Project Manager.*

- The *Supervisor* is

Name **Mr I Lookhard**

Address **Long Acre Industrial Estate**
Spearshead
Bristol
BS8 2LR

The *Supervisor's* role is essentially to check that the *works* are constructed an manufactured in accordance with the contract, including tasks similar to those of a resident engineer, a clerk of works and an in-factory inspector.
GN on "Supervisor"

Whilst normally located close to the construction site, for plant contracts wit considerable off site manufacture, the *Supervisor* may be represented by resident inspectors etc.

- The *Adjudicator* is

Name **Ms I Arkwright**

Address **Solva and Smith Project Management**
Meadow House
Goode Road
Exeter
EX8 6LN

The *Adjudicator* proposed by the *Employer* should be named here. Alternatively a list of acceptable names could be proposed. A name acceptable to both the *Employer* and the *Contractors* must be included here on the Contract Date.
GN on "Adjudicator"

The terms of his proposed appointment should be provided to tenderers.

- The Works Information is in
Parts 2, and 4 of the enquiry document

- The Site Information is in
Part 3 of the enquiry document

- The *boundaries of the site* are **shown on drawing SP/104 Revision 4**

The *boundaries of the site* could be stated in narrative form if this is more appropriate and clearly defines the area, for example, 'the area of land to the North of the *Employer's* Spearshead Works within a perimeter formed by the Al23 Filton Road, the unclassified Barn Lane and the Wessex Canal.'

- The *language of the contract* is **English**

- The *law of the contract* is the law of **England and Wales, subject to the jurisdiction of the Courts of England and Wales**

It is possible for English law (for example) to be applied in a foreign court. Thus the place of jurisdiction should be stated here are well as the *law of the contract.*

- The *period for reply* to a communication is **2 weeks**

The period for reply (GN's on CL 13.3 - 13.5) must give sufficient time for the parties to respond. The ECC seeks to encourage good management and an excessive period entered here will damage the principle of problem solving in 'real time'. If an *Employer* requires prompt action from the *Contractor* it is sensible that the *Employer* and *Project Managers* should also respond promptly.

Part one — Data Provided by the *Employer* (continued)

2. The *Contractor's* main responsibilities

- The *Contractor's* liability for Defects due to his design that are not listed on the Defects Certificate is limited to **£250,000**

The limit here only applies after the Defects Certificate has been issued. Before then there is no limit. If it is intended that there is no limit of the type provided by the clause the words 'unlimited' should be entered here.
GN on CL 21.5

3. Time

- The *starting date* is **1 October 1997**
- The *possession dates* are

Part of the Site	Date
1. **Contractor's compound**	**15 November 1997**
2. **Balance of the Site except existing main conveyor**	**30 November 1997**
3. **Exiting main conveyor**	**10 February 1998**

- The *Contractor* submits revised programmes at intervals no longer than **4** weeks

Revised programmes are submitted as stated in CL 32 but no longer than the intervals inserted here.
GN on CL 32

4. Testing and Defects

- The *defects date* is **104** weeks after Completion of the whole of the *works*

[T]his is the period the *Contractor* is liable [t]o correct Defects.
[G]N on section 4

- The *defect correction period* is **3** weeks

If the *defect correction period* is needlessly short it will increase the *Contractor's* risk of high costs (of standby stock, air freight etc.) which may lead to higher prices. For large projects it may be sensible to identify critical areas for which rapid repair/replacement is necessary and assign a shorter defect correction period than for non critical parts of the work.
GN on CL 43

5. Payment

- The *currency of this contract* is the **pound sterling (£)**

[I]t is recommended that the *assessment [i]nterval* does not exceed 5 weeks.
[G]N on CL50.1

- The *assessment interval* is **4** weeks
- The *interest rate* is **2%** per annum above the **average base rate in force from time to time at the following banks; Barclay's, Lloyd, National Westminster and the Royal Bank of Scotland.**

[It] is recommended that the *interest rate* is [n]ot less that 2% above the selected base rate.
[G]N on Cl51

6. Compensation Events

- The place where weather is to be recorded is **within the *boundaries of the site***
- The *weather measurements* to be recorded each month are
  - the cumulative rainfall (mm)
  - the number of days with rainfall more than 5mm
  - the number of days with minimum air temperature less that 0 degrees Celsius
  - the number of days with snow lying at **09:00** hours GMT
  - and these measurements:
    Working hours with windspeed exceeding 60km/hour

GN on CL 60.1 (13)

- The *weather data* are the records of past *weather measurements* for each calendar month which were recorded at **Lyneham, Wiltshire weather station**

  and which are available from **The Met Office, Building Consultancy Group, Johnson House, London Road, Bracknell, Berkshire, RG12 2SY, telephone 01344 856856 or fax 01344 854906**

WHERE NO RECORDED DATA IS AVAILABLE

- Assumed value for ten years return *weather data* for each *weather measurement* for each calendar month are:
  In part 5 of the enquiring document

This would not be used when a weather station is available.

8. Risks and Insurance

- The amount of the minimum limit of indemnity for insurance in respect of loss of or damage to property (except the *works*, Plant or Materials and Equipment) and liability for bodily injury to or death of a person (not an employee of the *Contractor*) due to activity in connection with this contract for any one event is **£2,000,000**

This is the minimum amount the *Contractor* must insure for.

- The amount of the minimum limit of indemnity for insurance in respect of death of or bodily injury to employees of the *Contractor* arising out of and in the course of their employment in connection with the contract is **unlimited**

The figures to be inserted in the insurance clauses need to be considered by the *Employer's* risk management and take into account local law applicable (for example to third party liability) at the site and working areas, as well as the law of the contract.
GN on Section 8

9. Dispute and Termination

- The person who will choose a new *Adjudicator* if the Parties cannot agree a choice is **the President for the time being of the Institution of Mechanical Engineers**

[G]N or CL 92.2

- The tribunal is **arbitration**

If it is intended to proceed directly to litigation if the adjudication is disputed the word **'litigation'** would be substituted for arbitration.

Optional Statements

If the *tribunal* is arbitration

GN on CL 93.2

- The arbitration procedure is **the Institution of Civil Engineers Arbitration Procedure (1983) or any amendment or modification to it in force when the arbitrator is appointed**

GN on CL 30

If the *Employer* has decided the *completion date* for the whole of the *works*

- The *completion date* for the whole of the *works* is **13 July 1998**

If the *Employer* is not willing to take over the *works* before the Completion Date

- The *Employer* is not willing to take over the *works* before the Completion Date

GN on CL 35.2

If no programme is identified in part 2 of the Contract Data

- The *Contrator* is to submit a first programme for acceptance within **3** weeks of the Contract Date

GN on CL 31.1

If the period for payment is not three weeks

- The period within which payments are made is **5** weeks

GN on CL 51.2

If there are additional compensation events

- These are compensation events
  1. **The port of Turkheim is closed due to ice for more than 5 weeks from 1 December 1997 and 1 March 1998**
  2. **A protected species is found on the site**

Additional compensation events should be included with caution and need to b[e] unambiguously defined. In example 2 here the definition of a protected speci[es] could prove contentious unless there ar[e] clauses in the Works or Site Information clarifying what is meant or the applicab[le] law provides a definition.
GN on CL 60

It may not be economical for the *Contractor* to assume a particular risk, even if damage is due to his negligence. In this example it is presumed that insurance of major damage to or loss of use of the main conveyor is more economically provided under arrangements the *Employer* can make. It is usually sensible for the *Contractor* to assume the risk up to a practical limit (in this case £3M) to encourage responsibility and due care. Alternatively if a single site insurance policy in the joint names of contractors and the *Employer* has been put in place this may deal with additional risks without the need to insert anything here.
GN on Section 8

If there are additional *Employer's* risks

- These are additional *Employer's* risks
  1. **Loss of use or damage to the main conveyor in excess of £3,000.000**

If the *Employer* is to provide Plant and Materials

- The insurance against loss of or damage to the *works*, Plant and Materials is to include cover for Plant and Materials provided by the *Employer* for an amount of **£150,000**

Insert value of "free issue" Plant and Materials to be incorporated into the *works*.
GN Section 8

If the *Employer* is to provide any of the insurances stated in the Insurance Table

- The *Employer* provides these insurances from the Insurance Table
  1. Insurance against **Loss of or damage to the works, Plant and Materials**

     Cover/indemnity is **£10,000.000**

     The deductibles are **£50,000**

If additonal insurances are to be provided

- The *Employer* provides these additional insurances
  1. Insurance against

     Cover/indemnity is

     The deductables are

State any additional insurances to be provided by the *Employer.* This will include single site policies and other special arrangements.
GN on Section 8

- The *Contractor* provides these additional insurances
  1. Insurance against **Contamination of feed before issue of Defects Certificate**

     Cover/Indemnity is **£100/tonne**

State any special extra insurances relevant to the contract that the *Contractor* is to provide.
GN on Section 8

Part one — Data Provided by the *Employer* (continued)

If Option B or D is used

- The *method of measurement* is **Civil Engineering (Edition....)**

  amended as follows **(none)**

If Option C or D is used

- The *Contractor's share percentages* and the *share ranges* are

Careful reading of the guidance notes on CL 53 is recommended before completing this statement *section.*

Share range	*Contractor's share percentage*
less than **80** %	**15** %
from **80** % to **90** %	**30** %
from **90** % to **110** %	**50** %
greater than **110** %	**20** %

If Option C, D, E or F is used

Forecasts for Actual Costs are a key tool for the *Project Manager's* use in controlling the cost of reimbursable/target contracts. The frequency needs to be sufficient to achieve this and would normally be on a 4 weekly cycle. GN on CL 20.4

- The *Contractor* prepares forecasts of Actual Costs for the *works* at intervals no longer than **4** weeks

GN on CL 50.6

- The *exchange rates* are those published in **The Financial Times** on **1 September 1995**

If Option G is used

- The amount of the performance bond is **£1,000.000**

GN on Option G

If Option J is used

- The amount of the advanced payment is **£100,000**

GN on CL J1.3

GN on CL J1.1

- The *Contractor* repays the instalments in assessments starting not less than **10** weeks after the Contract Date
- The instalments are **£10,000** (either an amount on a percentage of the payment otherwise due)

GN on CL J1.3

- An advanced payment bond is/~~is not~~ required

If Option K is used

- The *Employer* will pay for the items or activities listed below in the currencies stated

GN on Option K

Items and activities	Currency	Maximum payment
Weighing control system	**Japenese Yen**	**225,000 Yen**

- The *exchange rates* are those published in **The Financial Times** on **1 September 1995**

If Option L is used

- The *Completion* date for each section of the *works* is

GN on Option L

Section	Description	*Completion date*
1	**Unloading hopper**	**10 January 1998**
2	**Control system**	**20 February 1998**
3	**Diversion of existing conveyor**	**7 March 1998**
4	**Remainder of plant**	**13 July 1998**

Part one — Data Provided by the *Employer* (continued)

If Options L and Q are used together

- The bonuses for the *sections* of the *works* are

Section	Description	Amount per day
1	**Unloader hopper**	**Nil**
2	**Control system**	**Nil**
3	**Diversion of existing conveyor**	**£300**
4	**Remainder of plant**	**Nil**

There is no point in giving a bonus for early *Completion* unless ther is some va to the *Employer*. Thus in this example c the Completion that allows production commence/continue yeilds a bonus. GN on Options L and Q

If Options L and R are used together

GN on Option L and R

- Delay damages for the *sections* of the *works* are

Section	Description	Amount per day
1	**Unloader hopper**	**£200**
2	**Control system**	**£200**
3	**Diversion of existing conveyor**	**£400**

If Option N is used

- The proportions used to calculate the Price Adjustment Factor are

Proportion	linked to index for	prepared by
0.30	**Retail prices "All items", Table 6.4, 1 Jan 1995 = 100**	**Department of Employment**
0.20	**Average earnings, Mechanical Engineering Table 5.3, 1 Jan 1994 = 100**	**Department of Employment**
0.15	**Labour cost index (electrical) 1 Oct 1995 = 100**	**Conveyor Manufacturer Association**
0.25	**Electrical Machinery Index, Table 1SIC 32 Jan 1995 = 100**	**Department of Trade and Industry**
0.10	Non-adjustable	
1.00		

GN on Option N

- The *base date* for indices is **1 January 1995**

If Option P is used

- The *retention free amount* is **£250,000**
- The *retention percentage* is **10%**

GN on Option P

If Option Q is used

- The bonus for the whole of the *works* is **£2,500** per day

GN on Option Q

If Option R is used (whether or not Option L is also used)

- Delay damages for the whole of the *works* are **£2,000** per day

GN on Option R

Part one — Data Provided by the *Employer* (continued)

If Option S is used

- The amounts for low performance damage are

GN on Option S

Amount	Performance level
£50	for **each KVA power consumption above amount stated in tender**
£10	for **each kg/hour water consumption above amount stated in tender**

If Option V is used

- The *Trustees* are
  Name **Miss A Storm FCA**
  Address **Smith Storm and Partners**

  Name **Mr I Pay Llb Barrister**
  Address **Belmont Chambers**

Trustees should be chosen from several professional groups, but given the legal pitfalls it is recommended that - one should be experienced in insolvency law. GN on Option V

If Option Z is used

- The additional conditions of contract are ....

s accepted that the *Employer* will from ne to time need to include additional nditions. These should only be used en absolutely necessary.

mplex amendments to the ECC text ays creates a risk of conflict and onsistency with other conditions, and en the flexibility inherent in the ECC tem as written should only be made in y special cases.

not write additional conditions iting how the *Conractor* is to do the rk. These should always be put in the rks Information.
on Option Z

Part two — Data Provided by the *Contractor*

Statements given in all contracts

- The *Contractor* is:

  Name Woodstone Plant plc

  Address Construction House
  25 Western Avenue
  Exminster
  PR7 6NX

- The *fee percentage* is 10 %
- The *working areas* are the Site and Batching Plant at Workton Village as identified on drawing no XD3096
- The key people are

  (1) Name I K Brunel

  Job Construction Manager

  Responsibilities Overall responsibility for contract

  Qualifications C.Eng. M.I.C.E. M.I Mech.E.

  Experience 20 years in major construction (see enclosed CV)

Full legal name of *Contractor*.

Contractors address (this should be the address from which the *Contractor* expects to manage the contract - it need not be the registered office).

Include the post or other address code.

The *fee percentage* when applied to Actual Costs includes profit and any costs not included in the definitions of Actual Cost.
GN on CL 11.2(17)

Working areas in addition to the Site could be for example:
Fabrication yard
Concrete batching plant
Holding areas
(The *Contractor's* factory is not a working area).
GN's on Cl 15.1. 71.1 and SCC

Name key people: typically at least:
Director/Senior Manager
Contract Manager
Site Manager
Include a CV if appropriate.
GN on CL 24

The *Employer* should insert the appropriate optional statement for completion by tenderers into the tender documents.

Optional statements

If the *Contractor* is to provide Works Information for his own design

- The Works Information for the *Contractor's* design is in Tender Schedule W.I.

If the *Contractor* is required to submit pre tender design - the location of the drawings and specifications is recorded here.

Note: where any part of the design does not comply with the Works Information in part one of the Contract Data (the *Employer's* requirements). The latter has precedence. See 60.1.1).

If a programme is to be identified in the Contract data

- The programme identified in the Contract data is WI/101

Identify the programme - main purpose to inform how the *Contractor* intends to carry out the work and how it affects the *Employer's* other activities

If the *Contractor* is to decide the *completion* date for the whole of the *works*

- The *completion date* for the whole of the *works* is 1 June 1998

Inserted if the *Employer* wishes the *Contractor* to offer the *completion date* for the whole of the *works*. This may be for example the earliest or the most overall economical date. The *Employer* should indicate, for example in the instructions to tenderers, what is requir

If Option A or C is used

- The *activity schedule* identified WI/102

If Option A or C is used. (The *Employer* may provide a schedule for completion or require the *Contractor* to provide one based on activities stated in the instructions to tenderers).
See GN p23.

The *activity schedule* for Option A total up the price the *Employer* will pay.

The *activity schedule* will also normally used for Option C to determine the targ price.
See GN on Activity Schedule

If Option B or D is used

- The *bill of quantities* are enclosed WI/BOQ

The *bill of quantities* is priced and extended by tenderers to produce the tendered Prices.

The *Employer* must ensure that the chos method of measurement (e.g. by lump sum items) recognises the stated extent *Contractor* design and tenderers need to be particularly aware in contracts where the design liability is split between the parties that *Contractor* designed work w not be remeasured.
See GN on Bill of Quantities

If Option A, B, C or D is used

- The tendered total of the Prices is £3,050,000 (Three million and fifty thousand pounds sterling)

If Option A,B,C or D is used. Some *Employers* may require this total to be entered in the Form of Tender in which event the item may not appear here at all or alternatively read "The tendered total of the Prices is in the Form of Tender".

Part two — Data Provided by the *Contractor* (continued)

If Option A, B, C, D or E is used:

Data for Schedule of Cost Components

- The hourly rates for Actual Cost of manufacture and fabrication outside the Working Areas are

Category of employee	Hourly rate
Skilled	£10.50
Semi-skilled	£9.75
Unskilled	£9.25
Toolroom	£12.00

lude sufficient categories to enable sts of work outside the working areas be identified. Do not include overhead sts in the rate.

- The hourly rates for Actual Cost of manufacture and fabricatin overheads is 210 % except for Toolroom which is 350 %

It may be necessary to identify different overheads for specialist work or different factory locations.

- The hourly rates for Actual Cost of design outside the Working Areas are

Category of employee	Hourly rate
Tracer	£8
Draughts person	£19
Design engineer	£22
Senior design engineer	£26

- The percentage for design overheads is 25 %

nay be necessary to identify different erheads if both manual and CAD ilities will be used.

- The categories of employees whose travelling expenses to and from the Working Areas are included in Actual Costs are all design categories shown above

Not used with the Shorter Schedule of Cost Components

- Except for special items the percentage for Equipment depreciation and maintenance is 20 %

This percentage is to allow for maintenance to be included in Equipment costs. See SCC 22

The percentage is likely to have to allow for cost of replacement, financing modifications and upgrading. See GN on Percentage for Equipment depreciation and maintenance

- The percentages for depreciation and maintenance for special items of Equipment are:

Equipment	Size or Capacity	%

ude special equipment for which cial depreciation rates apply dredgers, drilling platforms.

- The percentage for Working Areas overheads is 20 %

plied to Actual Cost of people - see SCC for typical items included in this sum

Only used with the Shorter Schedule of Cost Components

- The percentage for **people** overheads is 50 %

Short method people overheads include extra items to the main schedule, i.e.

- components of cost of people listed in long method but excluded from short method.
- charges in 41, 42 and 43 of "long" method.
- a charge for overhead costs to replace the provision in 44 of the "long" method.

See GN on the Shorter SCC

- The published list of Equipment is the last edition of the list published by Federations of Civil Engineering Contractors

ipment % should be negative if lished rates exceed contractors costs.

- The percentage for adjustment for listed Equipment is -25 %
- The rates for other Equipment are

Equipment	Size or capacity	Rate

ude special equipment not covered by lished lists dredgers, special cranes, batching nt.

APPENDIX 6

Meteorological office notice

To obtain data, analysis or reports, etc., concerning past weather, contact the Met Office:

- England, Wales and overseas: The Met Office, Commercial Services, Johnson House, London Road, Bracknell, Berks RG12 2SY, tel. (01344) 856207, telex 849801, fax (01344) 854906
- Scotland: The Met Office, Saughton House, Broomhouse Drive, Edinburgh EH11 3XQ, tel. (0131) 244 8356, fax (0131) 244 8389
- **Northern Ireland**: The Met Office, 1 College Square East, Belfast BT1 6BQ, tel. & fax (01232) 328457
- **Specialist building enquiries**: The Met Office, Building and Construction Climatology Unit, Johnson House, London Road, Bracknell, Berks RG12 2SY, tel. (01344) 856856/856836, telex 849801, fax (01344) 854906
- **Specialist marine enquiries**: The Met Office, Marine Advisory and Consultancy Service, Johnson House, London Road, Bracknell, Berks RG12 2SY, tel. (01344) 854979/854978/854562/854981, telex 849801, fax (01344) 854906.

APPENDIX 7

Sample Trust Deed for use with the NEC Engineering and Construction Contract Kindly prepared by Nabarro Nathanson

(This Model should not be used without further legal advice.)

TRUST DEED

Dated 199

Parties

The Parties are the *Employer* and the *Trustees*
The *Employer* is [name, address]
The *Trustees* are [name, address]

Definitions 1

1.1 The following words have the meanings set out opposite them:

Beneficiaries

(1) The *Contractor* and
(2) The following who are employed to Provide the Works:

- Subcontractors;
- suppliers of the *Contractor*;
- subcontractors of whatever tier of a Subcontractor;
- suppliers of whatever tier of a Subcontractor or of any subcontractor of a Subcontractor;
- suppliers of whatever tier of a supplier of the *Contractor*.

Contract

A contract dated [ ] made between the *Employer* and the *Contractor* for the provision of the *works*, which are [ ].

Contractor

[name]

Deed

This Trust Deed

Insolvency

In the case of an individual, when he has:

- presented his petition for bankruptcy,
- had a bankruptcy order made against him.
- had a receiver appointed over his assets or
- made an arrangement with his creditors.

In the case of a company, when it has

- had a winding-up order made against it,
- had a provisional liquidator appointed to it,
- passed a resolution for winding-up (other than in order to amalgamate or reconstruct),
- had a receiver, receiver and manager, or administrative receiver appointed over the whole or a substantial part of its undertaking or assets or
- made an arrangement with its creditors.

Person — Any individual, *Trustees*, company, partnership or incorporated or unincorporated body.

Trust — The Trust established by this Deed.

Trustees — The *Trustees* of the Trust at the relevant time.

Trust Fund — A fund held and administered by the *Trustees* comprising the assets specified in Schedule 2, all additions of a capital nature to them and the assets from time to time representing them.

Trust Payment — Any payment or application of any part of the Trust Fund as the *Trustees* think fit.

Trust Period — The period ending on the day before the [tenth] anniversary of this Deed or on such earlier date as the *Trustees* specify by deed [but not retrospectively].

Unpaid Sum — The value of the payment which in the opinion of the *Trustees* the Beneficiary will not receive or is unlikely to receive in respect of the *works* as a result of the events referred to in subclause 3.3. That amount excludes any interest on such sum and excludes any payment in compensation for any other financial or other loss which may be suffered by the Beneficiary in consequence of such events.

1.2 Any word or phrase with capital initials or in italics not defined above has the same meaning as it has in the Contract, unless there are inconsistent definitions in the Contract and this Deed, in which case the definitions in the Deed take effect.

1.3 In this Deed, except where the context shows otherwise, words in the singular also mean in the plural and the other way round and words in the masculine also mean in the feminine and neuter.

1.4 Where the context admits, the word 'may' in conjunction with a verb indicates a discretion and its absence indicates an obligation.

General 2

2.1 The *Employer* is establishing this Trust in connection with the Contract and has placed under the control of the *Trustees* the assets specified in Schedule 2.

2.2 The *Employer* may add further assets to this Trust.

2.3 This Deed is irrevocable.

Trust Payments 3

3.1 The *Trustees* hold the Trust Fund on the following trusts.

3.2 If a Beneficiary complies with the conditions set out in subclause 3.3 the *Trustees* may at their discretion make a Trust Payment to that Beneficiary.

3.3 The conditions referred to in subclause 3.2 are that the Beneficiary shows to the satisfaction of the *Trustees*

- that he has not received all or part of a payment properly due to him under his contract relating to the Works, and
- that the reason for the failure to pay is the Insolvency of the person which should have made the payment.

3.4 The amount of a Trust Payment is not to exceed the Unpaid Sum.

The *Trustees* are not to make any Trust Payments in respect of any application received from a Beneficiary after the Defects Certificate has been issued in relation to the *works*.

3.5 Subject to subclause 3.4:

- the *Trustees* have entire discretion as to whether or not a Trust Payment is made and as to the amount and timing of any Trust Payment and the manner in which it is paid;
- a Trust Payment may take the form of a payment on account;
- the *Trustees* may take into account the result of any enquiries into the likely ability of the liquidator or trustee in bankruptcy of a person which is subject to Insolvency to meet the claims of unsecured creditors from funds in his hands;
- before making or agreeing to make a Trust Payment the *Trustees* may require a Beneficiary;
    - to assign to the *Trustees* on such terms as the *Trustees* think fit all its rights in relation to the receipt from another person of any sum to which the proposed Trust Payment directly or indirectly or in whole or in part relates, or
    - to give an undertaking to the *Trustees* in a form acceptable to them in relation to such sum;
- If a Beneficiary
    - has received a Trust Payment (whether or not as a payment on account or a conditional payment) and
    - receives a payment from another person to which a Trust Payment relates (whether in whole or in part and whether directly or indirectly)

then the *Trustees* may require the Beneficiary to repay the Trust Payment (or the appropriate proportion of it) promptly to the *Trustees*.

Income 4

Subject to the payment of any expenses of the Trust which are in the opinion of the *Trustees* attributable to income, the *Trustees* pay the income of the Trust Fund to the Employer for its own use free of these trusts.

Obligations of the parties 5

5.1 The Employer undertakes

- (if the Trust Fund is established by a payment) to maintain the Trust Fund at the Initial Value;
- (if the Trust Fund is established by guarantee) to ensure that the guarantor maintains the Trust Fund at the Initial Value;
- (if the Trust Fund is established by undertaking) that the undertaking is maintained at the Initial Value;

and in each case the Initial Value is for this purpose determined without taking into account any Trust Payments or any other payments which have been made out of the Trust Fund or any income.

5.2 The *Trustees* notify the *Employer* or the guarantor (as appropriate) in writing within one week of making a Trust Payment and the *Employer* restores (or ensures that the guarantor restores) the Trust Fund to the Initial Value within two weeks of notification.

5.3 The *Employer* notifies the *Trustees* of any Defects Certificate in relation to the Contract as soon as it is issued.

5.4 The *Employer* pays the *Trustees* their fees and expenses for administering the Trust Fund and pays any guarantor's fees.

5.5 The *Trustees* may engage professional advisers and consultants to help them with the administration of the Trust Fund and may make Trust Payment for their fees and expenses.

Ultimate application of Trust Fund 6

On the expiry of the Trust Period or, if earlier, when it appears to the satisfaction of the Trustees that:

- all payments in respect of the *works* have been made and
- no Beneficiary remains eligible for any Trust Payment and
- no repayment of a Trust Payment is due to the *Trustees*

the *Trustees* pay or transfer the Trust Fund (including any accrued income) to the *Employer* (or as the *Employer* directs) for the use of the *Employer* and free of these trusts. The *Employer* is responsible in exoneration of the *Trustees* for terminating any guarantee or undertaking.

Administrative powers 7

The *Trustees* have in addition and without prejudice to all statutory powers the powers and immunities set out in Schedule 1 but the *Trustees* may not exercise any of their powers so as to conflict with the above provisions of this Trust.

New trustees 8

The power of appointing new trustees is vested in the *Employer*.

Proper law 9

The Trust is governed by English law.

Arbitration 10

The *Trustees* may refer any dispute arising in connection with the Trust to a single arbitrator appointed by agreement between the *Trustees* and the person with whom they are in dispute; or failing such agreement in accordance with the Arbitration Procedure; or if there shall be none to a single arbitrator appointed by the President for the time being of the Institution of [   ].

IN WITNESS of which this Deed has been executed and was delivered on the date shown on page 1.

Schedule 1

ADMINISTRATIVE POWERS

Investment 1

The *Trustees* invest or apply the Trust Fund in one or more accounts in the names of all the Trustees with a bank or banks (being institutions authorised by the Banking Act 1987) in the United Kingdom. The *Trustees* may delegate power to sign on any account to any [two] of their number. The *Trustees* are not to invest the Trust Fund in any other way without the previous written consent of the Employer.

Advisers 2

The *Trustees* may employ professional advisers in connection with the Trust as they consider proper.

Expenses 3

The *Trustees* may pay taxes and other expenses out of capital or income as they consider proper.

Proxies 4

The *Trustees* may give proxies and powers of attorney for voting or acting on their behalf in relation to the Trust Fund or any part of it.

Indemnities 5

The *Trustees* may enter into any indemnity in favour of any person in respect of any liability in connection with the Trust.

***Trustees'* Interests 6**

Any *Trustee* may enter into any transaction concerning the Trust Fund even if such *Trustee* is interested in the transaction in any way other than as a *Trustee*.

***Trustees'* Charges 7**

In addition to reimbursement of proper expenses:

- any *Trustee* which is a trust corporation or company authorised to undertake trust business is entitled to payment for its services in accordance with the terms and conditions agreed between such *Trustee* and the *Employer*;
- any professional or business *Trustee* is entitled to payment of all normal charges for business done services rendered or time spent personally or by such *Trustee*'s firm in relation to the Trust including acts which a *Trustee* not engaged in any profession or business could have done personally.

***Trustee* Indemnity 8**

No *Trustee* is liable for any loss to the Trust Fund arising by reason of:

- the negligence or fraud of any agent employed by any *Trustee* even if the employment of such agent was not strictly necessary provided reasonable care has been exercised in choosing the agent.
- any mistake or omission made in good faith by any *Trustee* or
- any matter or thing except wilful fraud or dishonesty on the part of the *Trustee* who is sought to be made liable.

Variation 9

The *Trustees* may (having first obtained the written consent of the Employer and written advice from a person qualified in English law that such action would be expedient for the purposes of this Trust) by deed revoke or vary any of the provisions of this schedule or add any further administrative provisions as the *Trustees* think fit.

Schedule 2

INITIAL TRUST FUND

[[amount equal to Initial Value] cash]. . . . .

OR

The benefit of a guarantee for £ [Initial Value] provided by [bank etc] to the *Trustees* in the form of the copy document attached to this Deed and marked for identification by the *Employer* and the *Trustees* which the *Employer* agrees to assign to the *Trustees* if requested.

OR

The benefit of an irrevocable undertaking made by the *Employer* with the *Contractor* and the *Trustees* in the form of the copy document attached to this Deed and marked for identification by the *Employer* and the *Trustees* which the *Employer* agrees to assign to the *Trustees* if requested.

The Common Seal of [*Employer*] . . . .

was affixed to this Deed in the . . . .

presence of: . . . .

Director . . . .

Director/Secretary . . . .

OR

Executed as a Deed on behalf of [*Employer*]. . . . .

by [name] [Director] . . . .

and [name] [Director/Secretary] . . . .

OR

Executed as a Deed on behalf of . . . .

[*Employer* Partnership] . . . .

by [name] [Partner] . . . .

in the presence of the

witness named below:

Witness . . . .

Address: ....

....

....

Occupation ....

....

Executed as a Deed on behalf of ....

[public authority *Employer* ....

by [name] ....

and [name] [authorised signatories] ....

Executed as a Deed by [1st *Trustee*] ....

of the witness named below ....

Witness ....

Name: ....

Address: ....

....

....

Occupation ....

....

Executed as a Deed by [2nd *Trustee*]..

of the witness named below ....

Witness ....

Name: ....

Address: ....

....

....

Occupation ....

....